GOODBYE OLD FRIEND

GOODBYE OLD FRIEND

A Sad Farewell to the Working Horse

SIMON BUTLER

First published in Great Britain in 2012
Copyright © Simon Butler 2012

British Library Cataloguing-in-Publication Data
A CIP record for this title is available from the British Library

ISBN 978 0 85704 170 8

HALSGROVE
Halsgrove House,
Ryelands Business Park,
Bagley Road, Wellington, Somerset TA21 9PZ
Tel: 01823 653777   Fax: 01823 216796
email: sales@halsgrove.com

Part of the Halsgrove group of companies
Information on all Halsgrove titles is available at: www.halsgrove.com

Printed and bound in China by Everbest Printing Co Ltd

Contents

DEDICATION

for Isaac, Leila and Charlie

Foreword

It was originally my intention to tell the story of the decline of the horse from all aspects of British life from the nineteenth century onward, including those animals working on the land and the millions that were made to work in our growing cities.

From 1850 to the end of that century the population of Britain almost doubled, from around 13 million to 32 million. At the start of Victoria's reign London was already the world's largest city, By 1850 its population had grown three-fold, reaching over 3 million. Christened 'The Great Wen' by William Cobbett in 1820, London was indeed a place of social disfigurement and corruption, and the complex and often miserable story of horses that were brought to work here, and in other cities, is one that requires a book of its own.

While life in rural Britain could also be harsh, the environment was more conducive to the nature of horses, and their story thus more pleasant to tell.

The reason *why* these animals disappeared from our lives is quite simple – it is called progress. *How* this happened is, I hope, a story worth telling.

Simon Butler
Manaton 2012

Acknowledgements

Thanks are due to those who have inspired and encouraged me in the writing of this book, foremost my family and friends, General Sir Frank Kitson and Lady Kitson, to Mairi, Tom and Christian Hunt for photographs from their family albums, and to everyone at Halsgrove who have supported this project from the outset. Thanks also to Roger Fogg for his memories of the last days of farming with horses in Cornwall; to Paul Rackham who showed great generosity in allowing me to photograph his superb collection of tractors; and to Edward Knowles for his photographs of the Suffolks on the Somerleyton Estate. Special thanks to Bob Piggot for his information on equine veterinary care, and to Sheumais Webster, farrier. These two provided wonderful stories of their experiences with working horses deserving a book of their own.

The book would not have been possible without access to the thousands of photographs made available through the Halsgrove Community History Series, many of which appear in this book. My thanks go to the authors and contributors to this series, literally too many to mention by name, but I recommend readers to seek out the individual books. There are now over 220 titles in the series details of which can be found at www.halsgrove.com. Other photographs are taken from the author's personal collection.

Grateful acknowledgement is made to the following authors and their books: Alison Downes and Alan Childs *My Life With Horses*; Micky Mitchell (Maud Shire) *A Country War*; George Ewart Evans *Akenfield* and *Horse Power and Magic*; Peter Brears *The Old Devon Farmhouse*; Stephen Wood *Dartmoor Farm*; Cecil Torr *Small Talk at Wreyland*; F. C. Wigby *Just A Country Boy*; Guy Smith *A History of the NFU*; Edward Hart *The Suffolk Punch*; Alison Uttley *A Country Hoard*; Mollie Harris *From Acre End*; George Sturt *The Wheelwright's Shop*; Laurie Lee *Cider With Rosie*; A.L. Rowse *A Cornish Childhood*.

Preface

"The war of 1914–18 was the first and last global conflict in which the horse played a vital role. It was also the point at which the relationship between humans and horses could be said to have changed forever."

My book *The War Horses*, published in 2011, provided an historical overview of the fate of horses during the First World War. In it, I suggested that the war itself was a watershed, precipitating the decline of horses in the British landscape largely due to the rapid advances in technological development during the four years of that conflict. Such simple statements, while true in themselves, also hide more complex factors. The reality is that the writing on the wall for the demise of horse power was chalked up long before 1914, with the war itself, while providing a useful pivotal point for an examination of the subject, simply being the accelerant in that decline.

The subject is a fascinating one, for not only did the passing of the horse as the world's principal source of motive power draw a line under centuries of human/equine

Rivals in power. A Ferguson tractor moves off with a full load of grain sacks watched by an alert horse at Easton, Norfolk, in the 1950s. This was the decade in which horse power in the British farming landscape finally gave up its position to the tractor.

inter-dependence, it saw the passing of almost all the wisdom and knowledge that flowed directly from those bonds. Such knowledge, often imbued with near-mystical power, gave the horseman status in the community. As farmer John Grout tells Ronald Blythe in his celebrated work *Akenfield*:

> *The horsemen were the big men on the farm. They kept in with each other and had secrets. They were a whispering lot. If someone who wasn't a ploughman came upon them and they happened to be talking, they would soon change the conversation.*

In this book I concentrate on the period from mid Victorian times to the 1950s. I look mainly at the working horse in agriculture as it is this aspect of the disappearance of the horse we immediately think of, and which has engaged the attention of artists, writers and poets, often in the most sentimental of ways. The image created of a ploughman and his team breasting the gentle rise of a furrowed field, bathed in evening sunlight, is universally set in the British psyche. Such nostalgia is seldom matched by reality, the hours were long, pay was poor, and the work arduous and un-remitting:

> *In those days when the horse was king, all the work upon the farms was either done by hand or horse-drawn implements. During the dark winter months the men worked what was known as 'one journey' hours. Seven in the morning until twelve noon, ate their meal on the job and work again from half-past twelve until half past three in the afternoon: six days per week. In springtime, they worked 'two journeys'. Seven in the morning until noon, brought their horses in for 'bait'. Commenced work again at half-past one until six in the evening, five days a week. On Saturday they work from seven in the morning until twelve noon.*

Yet while machines have reduced the grim realities of labour, they have at the same time replaced, for many, the dignity of individual participation in their community through the erosion of timeless skills learnt at their father's knee.

Introduction

For centuries the horse was a status symbol, and remains so in a minor way even today. At modern Pony Club events the carefully clipped and accoutered, graded showjumper distinguishes its rider's social position from the owner of the game-but-dowdy little 'all rounder'. The controversy raging over fox hunting in Britain is as much one of social division as it is of the morality of animal welfare.

In the medieval period horses were categorised by their use rather than their breed; the knight on his charger, lords and ladies on their palfreys, and with carthorses and pack animals being in the care, but not in the ownership, of the labourer.

In war the quality of the horse was paramount, not only in its breeding and ability to withstand the rigours of battle, but as the use of armour increased, in its being able to carry the enormous weight of a fully equipped knight, along with its own protective armour and padding. These animals were the tanks of the medieval battlefield, steel-plated battering rams that ploughed their way through the ranks of foot soldiers. On the backs of these magnificent beasts Kings, Princes, Dukes and Lords, literally rose above the rank and file.

The legacy of such status, in part conferred by the quality of the horse one rides, continued well into the twentieth century, and in warfare was exemplified by the elite standing of cavalry forces which, during the First World War, retained their cachet despite their military obsolescence.

An early fifteenth century depiction of lords and ladies on a hunting trip, elegantly mounted.

An Edwardian hunt. Quality of breeding for men and women and horses counted.

A portrait by pre-eminent equine artist Alfred Munnings of General Seely and his horse Warrior, both heroes of the First World War, the last conflict in which status of a man and his horse counted for something on the battlefield.

On the domestic front in Britain, the gradual erosion of clear distinctions in social class began with the rise of the merchant classes – wealthy families who owed their status to the size of their bank accounts rather than their breeding. From the seventeenth century onwards fortunes were made abroad, from slavery, spices and general trading, which meant that the nation's wealth no longer rested in the hands of those connected to the court. Later, as Britain began to develop as the 'workshop of the world' mine owners, cotton manufacturers and their like added their names to this list of significant people.

Whereas in the past palaces and stately homes had been the province of royalty and the political elite, vast new estates were being bought up with 'new' money, and people in 'trade' forced their way into the corridors of power and influence. By the middle of Queen Victoria's reign these erstwhile parvenu families held the reins of much of the country's wealth. Along with their great houses went gardens and stables, farms and cottages; a nineteenth century reinvention of the feudal system.

There are few better examples of such families than the Gibbs whose spectacular Gothic house in Somerset, Tyntesfield, was built during the 1860s. William Gibbs became one of the richest commoners in England, his vast fortune built on importing guano, used as a fertilizer – bird droppings from islands off the coast of Peru.

The Gibbs, and other families like them, helped to break apart the centuries-old strictures of social status that predetermined one's 'place' in society. Their influence helped effect the rise of the middle class in Britain, a group who propelled themselves out of the working class by means of money and education, and with a desire to better themselves often cloaked in suffocating snobbery. Their homes mimicked the

Tyntesfield was built by 'commoner' William Gibbs with monies made from the importation of guano. Wealthy as he was, Gibbs could not escape the sneers of those who wished to remind him of the source of his fortune:

*'William Gibbs made his dibs
Selling the turds of foreign birds'*

grand houses of the upper classes, but in miniature, and they strove to provide themselves with the trappings of advancement. For the Victorian middle classes this included the means of transporting themselves. Few other facilities better define our class than the ability to move from place to place independently and at will. Ownership of a horse and carriage not only publicly signalled one's means to afford such a luxury, it mirrored the privileges the ruling classes had enjoyed for centuries.

Vicars, doctors, shopkeepers – indeed anyone with sufficient means – looked to equip themselves with any one of a vast variety of carriage types that coachmakers could provide, from brakes and broughams, dogcarts, gigs, jingles, phaetons, sociables, sulkies and traps. And of course each required at least one horse to pull it. Rapidly growing cities and towns and their suburbs echoed to the sounds of iron-shod wheels and the clop of hooves. Where inconvenience or cost prevented ownership, growing numbers of private companies provided horse-drawn transport for hire. As an indicator of social change in the mid Victorian period, the proliferation of the horse in the context of leisure and work has few equals, and the rapid rise and decline of the horse in the urban setting is worthy of a book in its own right.

In the countryside, change came less rapidly. While railways provided means for the mass transportation of people and goods, few people had the desire or the motivation for distant travel. Families usually lived within walking distances of one another, and a weekly trip to the nearest market satisfied any sense of wanderlust.

In exploring the demise of the horse, the humble bicycle should not be overlooked. While seldom replacing the horse as a mode of transport, bicycles provided a cheap and convenient means of getting around, especially as roads were improved. From the mid 1800s cycles opened up horizons for local travel and helped to break down the insular nature of rural life. Here, in 1869, a Mr Stuckey brings the first bicycle to Ottery St Mary in Devon, a wooden machine he built himself.

Towards the end of Victoria's reign many middle class families indulged themselves in the ownership of a smart pony and trap. Photographs taken around this time are posed much in the same way as present-day owners of a new car might celebrate by having their photo taken alongside it. Here the Reverend Skene with his wife Fanny and baby Nigel sit for the photographer at Homersfield, Norfolk.

13

Villagers from Hempnall in Norfolk on an outing to celebrate Queen Victoria's diamond jubilee in 1897. Farm carts have been pressed into service, the carthorses being given a day off from their work in the fields.

As Diarist Cecil Torr notes from his grandfather's journal of January 1846.

Like the rest of the farmers they see or know little beyond their own and parish affairs, and seldom go beyond their market towns, where they assemble and talk of the price of cattle and corn...'

Church and chapel outings happened once or twice a year, with perhaps a trip by train or a horse-drawn coach outing to the coast or nearby beauty spot.

The growth of the railways and, in particular, the appearance of steam traction engines, had a major effect on the way farming was carried out, but it was in the interest of landowners to keep the workers poor, with low wages and tied cottages just two of the means by which the farmworker and their families were held in thrall. It took a world war to change forever the face of farming in the countryside, patterns of life which had endured for centuries. And so, taking the period from around the start of Victoria's reign, during which the horse reached it's height with regard to its use in the countryside, and using the First World War as the pivotal point of decline, this book seeks to trace the eventual 'disappearance' of the working horse in Britain.

Opposite: A watercolour sketch 'Sunset' by Elizabeth Kitson SEA

14

The Horse on the Land

We still today talk of horsepower with little thought given to the origins of the term, yet it once had more definite meaning: that being the comparison of work done by a steam engine relative to a draught horse. It is ironic that the coining of the term which attempted to quantify the animal's power would eventually lead to the demise of the working horse.

We do not know the date at which man first domesticated the horse, although evidence points to this being around 4000BC in eastern Europe. Before that time wild horses were hunted by man, presumably for food, and prehistoric cave paintings dating from 30 000BC show this.

By the time of the Greeks and Romans, man's bond with the horse as a beast of burden and as a principal means of waging war was well established. In his *Book on Horsemanship,* c.400BC, the Athenian historian, Xenophon describes to his readers how best to judge a good horse and to train it, either for show or as a war horse.

15

In Britain it is likely that native pony breeds, surviving types of which can be found in Scotland, Wales and the Westcountry, served local Bronze and Iron Age tribes as pack animals and even as war horses. Certainly by the time of the Roman invasion we know that the natives were extremely proficient horsemen and charioteers, as Caesar describes in *The Gallic Wars*:

First of all the charioteers drive all over the field, the warriors hurling missiles; and generally they throw the enemy's ranks into confusion by the mere terror inspired by their horses and the clatter of the wheels. As soon as they have penetrated between the troops of [their own] cavalry, the warriors jump off the chariots and fight on foot. The drivers meanwhile gradually withdraw from the action, and range the cars in such a position that, if the warriors are hard pressed by the enemy's numbers, they may easily get back to them. Thus they exhibit in action the mobility of cavalry combined with the steadiness of infantry; and they become so efficient from constant practice and training that they will drive their horses at full gallop, keeping them well in hand, down a steep incline, check and turn them in an instant, run along the pole, stand on the yoke, and step backwards again to the cars with the greatest nimbleness.

It is reasonable to assume therefore that these same animals would be used for more domestic tasks, for fetching and carrying, and perhaps for work in the fields. While it is likely that some kind of simple wooden scratch plough existed earlier, the Roman occupation of these islands would certainly have offered its inhabitants access to a more sophisticated iron plough.

At this time the preferred animal for pulling the plough was not the horse but the ox, and this persisted beyond the Norman invasion, throughout the Middle Ages and well into the eighteenth century. That medieval manuscripts often depict the toil of the ploughman and work on the land throughout the year remind us that these activities were once a part of everyone's daily life – the repetition of 'the seedtime and the harvest' defining the calendar of their days.

Dartmoor ponies. Efforts are being made to maintain the pure breeds of British native ponies many of which have been subject to interbreeding. They generally exhibit the characteristics of the original stock, small, hardy with the ability to survive on rough grazing.

Ploughing in East Anglia with a team of four yoked oxen. From the Luttrell Psalter an illuminated manuscript dated c.1330, held in the British Library.

But, and this is a question keenly debated among agricultural historians, why did the horse eventually overtake the ox as the principal means of motive power? The Domesday survey of 1086 suggests that over 95 per cent of draught animals on the land were oxen, with mules and donkeys also recorded. It is assumed from this that the horse, where kept, was used primarily for riding rather than farm work. In the century following the numbers of horses kept as draught animals began to climb steadily despite the exhortations of agrarian writers such as Walter of Henley who, in his *Le Dite de Hosebondrie*, written around 1280, showed that horses were four times more costly to keep than oxen.

Thereafter the horse v. ox question remained a hot topic amongst agrarians, each citing reasons in support of their particular case; the cost of purchase, the expense of feeding, the ease of training and so on. As late as 1776 Lord Kames, in *The Gentleman Farmer*, makes an impassioned plea for the continued use of oxen over horses:

There is not any other improvement that equals the using of oxen instead of horses. They are equally tractable and they are fed and maintained at much less expense...

As with the decline of the horse in farming, so the demise of oxen as a means of motive power on the land was the result of a combination of factors occurring at the same time. Arguments in favour of their practical value over the horse came to nothing as within a few decades in the early 1800s oxen became an increasingly rare sight. But, as with the horse a century later, a small number of farms continued to use oxen, as here at John Dixon's Hall Farm at Hindringham, Norfolk. Here c.1905, we see farmworker Tom Dent with his oxen Nelson and Trimmer.

One of the disadvantages said to have led to the demise of working with oxen was the difficulty in shoeing them in comparison to the horse, contrary to Lord Kames' belief. The latter animal was far more compliant in allowing itself to be shod and was able to stand on three legs thus allowing the farrier to fit the shoe. This photograph certainly give credence to the suggestion that shoeing an ox was time-consuming and fraught with problems. Taken at Camborne in Cornwall, possibly as late as the 1920s, the animal is secured by ropes in a makeshift pen of four huge elm logs, while the foot is lashed to a horizontal post to allow the farrier-smith to attach the metal shoe.

What warms me to this subject is the great consumption of oats by workhorses, which would be totally saved by using oxen... I begin with affirming that an ox is as tractable as a horse and as easily trained to a plough or a cart. I have seen a couple of them in a plough going on sweetly without a driver as a couple of horses, directed by the voice alone without a rein. Oxen beside are preferable for a steady draught as they always pull to their strength without flinching, horses on the contrary are apt to stop when they meet with unexpected resistance... It is sufficient employment for a man to manage four or five horses, he will manage with equal ease double the amount of oxen. The shoeing of a horse is no inconsiderable expence, the expence of shoeing an oxen is a mere trifle.

While many others agreed with these comparisons, and indeed it was not unusual to see oxen and horses working together in a single team under the plough or when

carting, the fact remains that between c.1800 and the middle of that century oxen in British farming more or less disappeared, and it is no coincidence that this occurred alongside major reforms in agriculture, population growth and the migration towards cities, expanding industrialisation, and the concomitant dynamics in a society that called increasingly for more speed. Factors that later applied to the demise of the horse.

Nimbler, more responsive, and all-round a more versatile power source, the horse won out over its rival despite all the efforts of those who championed the ox. The horse collar, introduced into Europe around 900AD, had long been known to be more efficient than the yoke as a way of translating an animal's power kinetically. By the nineteenth century a host of other improvements to horse harness, the technology of shoeing, and the development of more efficient ways of connecting the horse to various implements and carriages, came together and collectively they gave the horse its unrivalled position in farming.

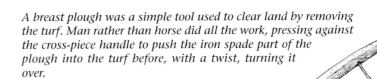

Ploughing with oxen. A miniature from an early-sixteenth-century manuscript of the Middle English poem 'God Spede ye Plough'.

Driving all this development was the need for more food to satisfy a growing population. At the start of the so-called Agricultural Revolution in the early sixteenth century, the population of England was around 4 million, and by 1800 had doubled in size, and doubled again in the next 50 years. By 1900 the population in England was almost 8 times greater than it had been in 1600, with 10 times the number of inhabitants who had witnessed William the Conqueror's arrival.

At the forefront of those who are said to have sparked the Agricultural Revolution into life are Lord 'Turnip' Townshend (1674-1738), Jethro Tull (1674-1741), Thomas Coke of Holkham (1754-1842), Robert Bakewell (1725-1795) and Arthur Young (1741-1820). History has given to these men an iconic status not always deserved, but it is true to say that they played a role in the mass movement towards improved systems of cropping and the selective breeding of livestock. Coupled to this was the dramatic sweeping aside of common rights to land which then allowed 'improvers' to carry out their new methods.

A breast plough was a simple tool used to clear land by removing the turf. Man rather than horse did all the work, pressing against the cross-piece handle to push the iron spade part of the plough into the turf before, with a twist, turning it over.

A Derby plough, dating from the mid nineteenth century, was a later development from the traditional all-wooden implement, being constructed entirely of iron except for the beam and handles. A small wheel regulated the depth of the furrow. It could be used with either horses or oxen.

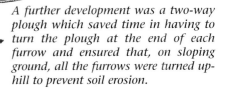

A further development was a two-way plough which saved time in having to turn the plough at the end of each furrow and ensured that, on sloping ground, all the furrows were turned uphill to prevent soil erosion.

19

Advocates of the use of oxen and bullocks in farming cite their advantages over the horse, among them their steadiness in pulling power. As one champion of oxen put it: 'They are less expeditious than horse in galloping or trotting it is true, but as farm work is performed in stepping, let the step of an ox and a horse be compared and the ox will be found not to be inferior especially where an ox is harnessed like a horse. As an ox is cheaper than a horse so he is fed cheaper in proportion, he requires no corn and he works to perfection on cut grass in the summer and hay in the winter, he does well even out of oat straw. Thus by using oxen a farmer can make money out of his whole crop of oats except what is necessary for his own family.' In addition oxen had a longer working life and at the end of their days provided meat and hides that could be sold. The photograph shows bullocks attached to a high gallows plough at High Noon Farm, Blofield, Norfolk in 1895. That the ploughman is mounted on one of the animals gives credence to the claim that these animals were as tractable as the horse.

This is 'Dashing Duke' one of the Shire horses kept at Bransford Court in Worcestershire the 1890s. In size and power such animals could not be described as second best to oxen and for fleetness of foot, for the carriage of produce around the farm and to market they had no equal, especially on poor road surfaces.

In contrast to the assertions made concerning longevity, Lord Kames states his own opinions on the working span of horses v. oxen: 'A horse put to work at the age of five years may endure hard work for twelve years, an ox is put to work at the age of four and at seven is in his prime which is the proper time to put him to the shambles.'

Whereas in the past the growing of crops and breeding of animals had been part of an organic process aimed at providing food for individual families and small communities, farming was now becoming part of a general intensification of agricultural production based on improved crop yields, larger animals and the incorporation of more and more land into the farming sphere. And powering this revolution was the horse.

Yet more dramatic than the events surrounding the revolution in agriculture was the Industrial Revolution which marked a turning point in history from the period 1750 to around 1850. Running hand in hand with the advances in the approach to agriculture, the wave of change that began in Britain and then swept across Europe and the rest of the world, unlocked the centuries-old ties to an economy hitherto fettered by manual labour and the power of draught animals.

The result of the introduction of steam-powered machines is covered later in this book where we will look at the effect that the development of factory production processes, improvement in roads and the rise of rail transport had on the use of horses. But farmers and farming have long been cautious about change, and throughout much of Victoria's reign, the agricultural landscape altered little. This was less to do

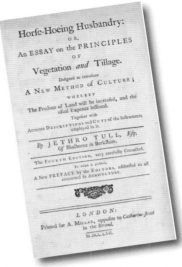

The title page of Jethro Tull's Horse-Hoeing Husbandry *first published in 1731. The book had a significant influence on the development of farming in Britain as did the author's invention of the seed drill and, later, the horse-drawn hoe. Tull held the belief that nutrients in the soil could be released by pulverisation thus making the use of fertilizers unnecessary. The photograph below, taken on the edge of Dartmoor in the 1880s reveals that even at that late date the old methods of clearing ground and fertilising the soil were still being practiced. Known as beat-burning, the turf is removed from the ground, burnt and re-applied as alkaline-rich ash on the acid moorland soil.*

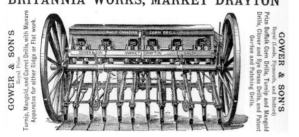

ROYAL AGRICULTURAL SOCIETY'S
PRIZE CORN AND SEED DRILLS,
MANUFACTURED BY
A. W. GOWER & SON,
BRITANNIA WORKS, MARKET DRAYTON

The seed drill (above) and the 'rear discharge' binder appeared as illustrations in a catalogue of 1894 including the most innovative farming machinery. While the ingenuity of these labour-saving implements and techniques of manufacture were at the cutting edge of technology, they still relied on horse power to propel them.

with a natural reticence or resistance to the 'new' – it's simply that farming is governed by the patterns of the years; the effects of dramatic seasonal variations which cannot be predicted being countered by traditional responses, intuitive and circumspect. The 'improvers', while overlooking the costs that would come from changes to existing implements or the purchase of new machinery, criticised the farmers for their slowness in adapting to change:

Men are led in chains by custom and fettered against their better interests. "Why should we pretend to be better than our fathers?" they will say modestly.

Then as now, men are reluctant to change unless driven to do so and it was to be another factor that eventually drove through the innovations in farming – the increasing cost of labour as workers left the land to seek less arduous work and to rid themselves of the iniquitous system of tied houses which gave landlord-farmers complete control over the lives of farmhands and their families. Such workers were at the mercy of their employers who could, without notice, lower their wages, or turn them out of their home if they fell out with them or felt they could no longer afford to employ them, or if they had become too old or too sick to work.

Then, with the development of lighter and more efficient steam engines in the nineteenth century, and the invention of the self-binder in 1879, came the spectre of even more men being thrown out of work, leading in the 1830s, to the Swing Riots in which labourers demanded a minimum wage, and tithe and rent reductions. This was the first such mass demonstration by agriculture labourers who took to smashing and burning engines and threshing machines.

Writing towards the end of the nineteenth century, Henry Rider Haggard, agricultural reformer and author of novels, among them *King Solomon's Mines*, recognised that the workers' emigration from the land was never to be reversed:

For centuries the source of power in agriculture was men and animals, principally the horse and the ox. The introduction of the steam traction engine around the mid nineteenth century had little initial effect on the amount of manual labour required. Men and boys as young as twelve encountered a life of hard work, low wages, with few holidays – conditions that persisted throughout the nineteenth century despite the legalisation of trades unions in 1824. Courts then invoked an obscure law preventing the swearing of oaths among groups of workers and this led to the transportation of the Tolpuddle Martyrs in 1834. These photographs help illustrate, even at the end of the 1900s, the numbers of men employed on a farm. Left: A team of men with scythes and whet stones are employed to mow hay in Seaton, Devon in 1909. Below: Farmworkers from an estate in Burnham Market, Norfolk c.1900.

Workers at Pittescombe Farm near Tavistock in Devon c.1900. The average size of farms in the area would be under 100 acres, larger farms such as Pittescombe at over 200 acres required five heavy horses and half a dozen labourers as seen here.

Two horses pull a newly-purchased seed drill at a Winscombe farm in Somerset, photographed around 1900. Refined by Jethro Tull in 1701 seed drills did not become commonplace on farms until the mid nineteenth century. The horse on the left is pulling a tine harrow, used to reduce the ploughed earth to a finer tilth.

The labourers 'back to the land'. That is the cry of the press and the fancy of the people. Well, I do not think that they will ever come back; certainly no legislation will ever bring them. Some of the rising generation may be induced to stay, but it will be by training them to the use of machinery and paying them higher wages. It should be remembered that the most intelligent men have gone; these will never come back, but the rising generation may stay as competition in the town increases, and the young men of the country are better paid. It should be remembered too that as many men as formerly are not required to till the land. During the last three years, by use of the self binder I have seen five men gather in the harvest on this farm [Wickham Market, Norfolk] instead of seven. Other labour-saving machinery will be introduced.

Just twenty years later the consequences of the First World War would set a seal on Rider Haggard's gloomy predictions. In 1840 only 20 per cent of the working population was employed in agriculture, dropping to 12 per cent in 1880 and, by the middle of the next century, to 5 per cent. In terms of actual numbers employed, the decline appears much less sharp, and in the century from 1850 the farming workforce fell from 1.2 million to 1 million. These falling numbers are more dramatic when the overall population growth, and consequently the total workforce is taken into

A pair of heavy horses pull a reaper-binder through a cornfield c.1915. These machines combined into one process the age-old traditions of cutting the crop by hand and gathering into sheaves the fallen stalks. Cumbersome and temperamental, and of many differing types, they saw the end of teams of reapers and reduced the numbers of workers at harvest time. In Akenfield, Ronald Blythe reports: 'Two and a half million acres of arable became grass between 1872 and 1900 and the cornlands which remained needed far fewer workers because of the invention of the binder and other machines.' In this photograph, helpers take a break from gathering the sheaves which have been tied loosely with twine automatically as they leave the binder, to be 'stooked' to dry.

Farmworkers at Marshwood in Somerset c.1900. The photograph indicates the labour-intensive nature of farming even at this date. Each worker holds the tool of his trade, from the wagon boy holding a whip, to a scythe, rakes, a dung fork, a thatcher's smoothing board, mattocks and a shepherd's crook. Note the hobnailed boots worn by the two workers sitting on the ground and the varieties of headgear.

account, and when bearing in mind that while the acreage under arable production fell from 60 per cent to under 40 per cent between 1870 and 1930, by 1950 it was back up to its mid nineteenth century peak.

Unrest among agricultural labourers, their gradual unionisation and improved conditions, did little to slow the pace of decline in the numbers employed in farming. Likewise, although from 1870 until the turn of the century there was a slight year-on-year increase in horses used in agriculture, their numbers steadily declined after 1900, falling from 834 000 in that year to 469 000 in 1940. Much of this decline in men and animals was down to the increased use, first of steam engines and later petrol and diesel engines. Here there is an added irony in the fact that just as the technological development of steam engines was reaching its peak, so the scientific breeding of heavy horses had also come into its own. Prior to the eighteenth century draught horses were bred to produce general characteristics suitable for heavy work. In earlier centuries the best of these beasts would have been selected for warfare and it is from this lineage which many of our heavy horses spring.

Today we tend to use general terms such as cart horse or shire horse to describe such animals but distinct breeds grew out of the careful selective breeding of distinct stock that led to breeds such as the Shire, the Suffolk Punch, Clydesdales and Percherons becoming established in Britain.

In his book *The Suffolk Punch*, the late Edward Hart, traces the history of the breed from the eighteenth century to the present day. The pedigree of these animals is

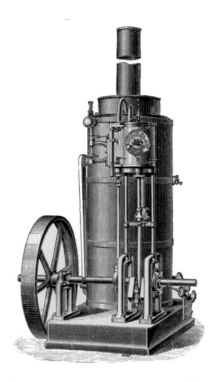

Stationary steam engines such as this were reaching the peak of their efficiency by the end of the nineteenth century and were replacing a number of tasks that otherwise would have been undertaken by horse-driven machinery, particularly the horse whim, used to drive chaff cutters and corn mills. They also reduced the numbers of men needed for farmwork, and between 1871 and 1881 over 200 000 workers emigrated to seek new opportunities in countries such as Canada and Australia.

'Mr Badham's Chester Emperor', one of the many illustrations from The Suffolk Stud Book *used to show the requisite conformity of the breed and the standards expected of the breeders in the nineteenth century.*

Horse power was adapted to more than just pulling a plough or cart, and the quest to breed ever stronger horses gathered momentum in the nineteenth century. Horse gins (gin being short for engine), or whims, used the motion of horses walking in a circle to generate, through shafts, cogs and drive belts, energy to power machinery such as corn mills, apple crushers and presses, chaff cutters, threshing machines and even saw benches. This photograph, taken c.1910 shows an uncovered horse walk at Mount Wise Farm near Stithians in Cornwall. The horses turned a central pivot-wheel which through a shaft drove a corn grinder inside the adjacent barn. Variations on how these were worked differed from region to region, as did their names: gin circle, gin gang, ginny-ring, horse course, horse gang, horse path, horse track and horse walk are all used.

Author and photographer Stephen Woods included this photograph of nineteenth-century horse gear at Batworthy Farm in his book Dartmoor Stone. He records: 'The horse gear comprised an axle, set vertically in a stone footstep, forming the centre of a large spur wheel which turned the mechanism through a series of cog wheels. The horse was harnessed to an arm below the spur-wheel. There was not much room and the farmer there recalled how sparks would fly when the horse's shoes struck the wall as it went by.'

contained within the pages of the *Suffolk Stud Book*, first published in 1880 by Herman Biddell and, according to Hart, it 'outclasses any other stud, flock or herd book of any class of stock anywhere in the world.'

Stallions and mares of good pedigree were in high demand, with the best of them rarely being put behind a wagon or plough. These were show horses, put to stud and owned by wealthier farmers and squires. Stallions would be taken from farm to farm in order to sire foals in the prevailing spirit of 'improvement' of the breed. The Suffolk's rise to fame was based on its 'never say die' attitude when faced with a task seemingly beyond its powers, and trials of strength between champion horses became common, as an advertisement at Harleston in Norfolk in 1766 relates:

This is to give notice that on the 8th of this instant March, there will be drawings for stallions at the house of John Hamblen, called the Magpie, for a silver cup value five guineas, no more than seven to enter, and not less than five. Each horse to draw single, to raise the most weight. The best of twenty pulls, and for every blank, to have a bushel of sand laid on the wagon.

George Ewart Evans in *The Pattern Under the Plough* records that while this sport was in its heyday in the eighteenth century it lasted well into the next. He relates that horsemen taught the Suffolk Punch to go down on its knees to exert its full strength in a dead-pull; 'that is, in pulling a loaded tumbril or wagon that had its wheels blocked to make the pull more difficult'.

The size and quality of horses used for farm work varied considerably. 'Prince' (on the left), photographed on a Dartmoor farm in the 1890s is perhaps more typical of a horse in working trim than the carefully groomed animal seen above which took second prize at the Minehead Horse Parade in 1908.

Opposite: An adaptation of the horse walk was to construct a building in which the horses could work to drive the gin. The obvious design was to make these buildings circular. and the horse-engine house (variously named, wheelhouse, roundhouse, horse-mill and gin gang), became a common feature on farms from the late eighteenth century. Other engines included the treadmill in which the walking horse drove an endless inclined plane over a set of rollers.

Opposite page top, left to right: A thatched round house at West Farm Winterborne Whitechurch, Dorset. A horse-powered mill for crushing cider apples at Mill House near Leigh in Worcestershire. A three-horse treadmill. Main picture: A pair of horses working in a roundhouse at Wingstone Farm on Dartmoor in 1915.

This heavy horse 'Tom' dwarfs the boy who stands holding its bridle. The animal was adjudged to have been the best dressed horse at the Watchet Horse Show in 1910.

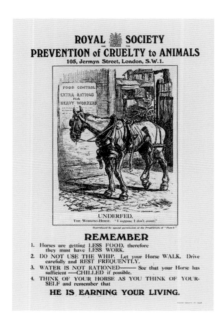

In the 1820s the first anti-cruelty bill was introduced into Parliament by Richard Martin MP, better known as 'Humanity Dick'. His aim was to reduce the cruel treatment of farm animals – specifically making it an offence to 'wantonly beat, abuse or ill-treat' any 'horse, cow, ox, heifer, steer, sheep or other cattle'. Two years after the Act was passed in 1822, Martin and his supporters created the Society for the Prevention of Cruelty to Animals, the first of its kind in any country, and which became the RSPCA in 1840 after being granted royal status by Queen Victoria.

While farmers and horsemen often took great pride in their horses and in showing off the skills associated with their work, the standard of animals often fell somewhat below that of the best of the pure-bred animals. And, while it was in the farmers' interest to take care of their working horses, and most did, neglect and overwork to the point of cruelty was not unheard of, as this report from the *Bury Free Press* newspaper of 1894 records:

David Bull was charged with cruelty to a horse at Melford, the animal was seen by Inspector Jones at Sudbury, it was dreadfully emaciated, defendant promised to have it killed but he was seen working it again by P.S. Reeve at Cavendish, he said it had running sores, another witness said he found it in a lane at Melford dead. As defendant who has previous convictions before was sentenced to 1 month's hard labour.

The rise of the animal welfare charities is covered in some detail in *The War Horses*, the companion volume to this work, and there is no doubt that where great poverty existed in the countryside, so were horses more likely to be subject to cruel abuse.

There was no single recognised way of acquiring a horse and breaking a young animal to pull a plough or cart. On small farms, and where there was no existing suitable stock from which to breed, it would be left to the farmer's experience to purchase an animal – an undertaking fraught with difficulties if nineteenth-century writers on the subject are to be believed. Horse fairs and local markets were traditionally the places to seek out new animals but the buyer had to be wary as canny vendors had tricks up their sleeve to fool buyers into believing they were looking at the perfect horse. Lameness was disguised, intractable horses drugged to appear placid, and elderly horses made to look younger.

The author was told of an instance when a farmer bought what appeared to be a very friendly mare off a vendor whom the horse constantly nuzzled affectionately, only later to discover the horse had a tendency to bite. He was told that the seller had hidden the caul (birth membrane) from a new-born foal in the top pocket of his jacket and it was this that the horse he'd bought could smell.

A small library of books and pamphlets appeared during the nineteenth century giving detailed advice to would-be horse owners, not only on what to look for in a good horse, but on treating diseases, feeding, grooming and shoeing. Writing in 1866 one such author offers some practical advice:

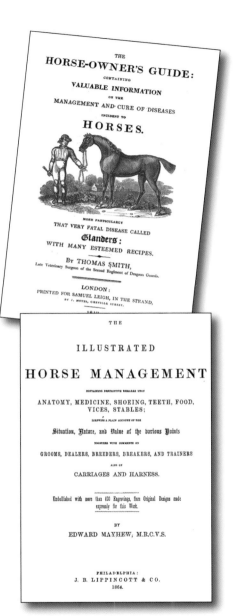

Above: Title pages to nineteenth century guides on the purchase, care and management of horses.

Left: Bampton Fair c.1910. The fair was originally famed for its sheep sales, but by the mid 1850s ponies and horses became the main focus.

Bakewell horse fair in 1910, held outside the Castle Inn.

Several persons are advertising books for taming wild horses and other persons are going about teaching the art to classes in private. Why do so many fail? The whole secret lies in this, that many persons can never handle a horse, with all the instruction in the world – it is not in them. To be a successful horse trainer he must have sympathy with the horse and a personal power of control.

Certain wealthier farmers undertook more selective breeding from their own stock, often retaining brood mares and employing the services of a stallion brought in from a local farm. These animals were taken from farm to farm by stallion walkers or leaders, men who had a leaning towards the management of these huge animals and an understanding of the process needed to encourage them to mate successfully. Jack Juby was a famous stallion walker in East Anglia, and one of the last, working in the 1940s and 50s when many of the old practices were dying out. It was a competitive business with various stud farms and their stallions vying for business, as Jack relates:

On Dereham market place on a Friday there would be seven of us the first week of the season, the horses all braided-up and plaited-up, and with a pocket-full of cards with details of the name of the stallion and where you were going to stop at certain nights. The farmers would look round them – you'd walk them up and down. Then we used to go into the 'Bull' and feed the horse, and in the afternoon you'd go up and down again.

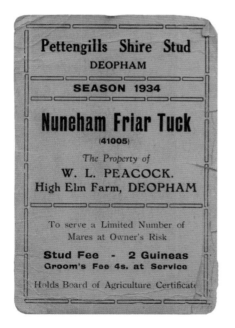

Pettengills Shire Stud

DEOPHAM

SEASON 1934

Nuneham Friar Tuck

(41005)

The Property of

W. L. PEACOCK.

High Elm Farm, DEOPHAM

To serve a Limited Number of
Mares at Owner's Risk

Stud Fee - 2 Guineas
Groom's Fee 4s. at Service

Holds Board of Agriculture Certificate

A stud card advertising the services of the stallion Nuneham Friar Tuck at 2 guineas.

Printed cards bearing the name of the stud, the stallion and the fee charged for its services were handed out to prospective customers, with the stallion walker receiving a separate 'groom's fee'. Nor was that the only perk of the job. These walkers gained much the same reputation as travelling salesmen and one such walker was said to have 'sired more foals' in the region than his stallion!

Gypsies, or travellers, have long been held to be discerning judges of horse flesh and many a farm horse was purchased through their hands. Jack recalls a little freelance activity:

Every year, about three or four times, there'd be these gypsies. They all had horses then – biggish cobs, and there'd be one or two you knew you were going to see. They'd be sleeping along the way and they'd got a mare and they'd want it serviced. You used to get a pound for that, and it didn't go in the books you see!

Each year Jack would attend the horse sales:

There would be a sale in March every year and your governor, he'd send a couple of horses. Somebody would be there wanting a certain horse. You'd take the horses to the sale and put them in

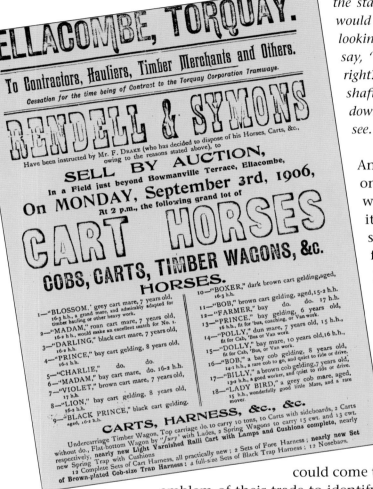

ELLACOMBE, TORQUAY.

To Contractors, Hauliers, Timber Merchants and Others.

Cessation for the time being of Contract to the Torquay Corporation Tramways.

RENDELL & SYMONS

Have been instructed by Mr. F. Drake (who has decided to dispose of his Horses, Carts, &c., owing to the reasons stated above), to

SELL BY AUCTION,

In a Field just beyond Bowmanville Terrace, Ellacombe,

On MONDAY, September 3rd, 1906,

At 2 p.m., the following grand lot of

CART HORSES

COBS, CARTS, TIMBER WAGONS, &c.

HORSES.

the stalls and do their tails up. Farmers would come along and they would be a-looking through the catalogue and they'd say, 'Well, wass he done, boy? Is he alright? Is he quiet? Has he been in the shafts?' Then you'd walk him up and down and they give you sixpence tip, you see.

And in earlier centuries it was not only the services of the horses that were for hire. Hiring fairs, where itinerant farmworkers put themselves forward in the hope of finding jobs, were held twice a year in spring and autumn. These fairs had their roots in medieval England when the Black Death killed around a third of the population and farmworkers were consequently in short supply. In order to control the supply of labour, hiring fairs came into being at which those seeking work and the employers could come together. Each worker carried an emblem of their trade to identify themselves. For the horseman, carters and waggoners this was a piece of whipcord worn on their hat or lapel. Those hired, if they were single, could be taken in as farm servants which meant their accommodation was provided and they would share their meals with the farmer and his family. In *Far From the Madding Crowd* Thomas Hardy describes the scene at a hiring fair:

At one end of the street stood from two to three hundred blithe and hearty labourers waiting upon chance. Among these, carters and waggoners were distinguished by having a piece of whip cord twisted round their hats; thatchers wore a fragment of woven straw; shepherds held their sheep-crooks in their hands; and thus the situation required was known to the hirers at a glance.

Suffolk horseman Tom Hiskey in 1871, aged 22. Note the whip, carried as much a sign of his trade as for actual use, and the high buttoned knee boots.

GOODBYE OLD FRIEND

While the novelist's account describes the scene in picturesque terms the reality was that the system of hiring generally worked in favour of the landowner, with the hired labour tied to the terms offered for the period agreed upon, usually a year, with little say in the conditions once they arrived on the farm. George Ewart Evans recorded what 'living in' meant for one worker on a Norfolk farm in the late 1900s.

My father used to live in at a farm in St Andrew's. There was a head horseman, second man and third man lived in there – and a boy. They used to have their tea about eight o'clock at night; they knew every day what they were going to have for their meals, every day they knew what they were going to have: the same old rations week after week. And to keep warm in winter time they used to – one got on a horse's back, and one on another, and another – and so on. They used to lay there to keep themselves warm until it was time to turn the horses out into the yard at night; then they'd go in for tea.

Historians owe a huge debt to Evans, and his book *Horse Power and Magic* is essential reading for those wishing to discover more about the use of horses on the land and their eventual decline. In particular, he explores the 'magic' surrounding horse lore and the arcane practices of the elite horsemen, drawing parallels between the customs existing in East Anglia and in North-East Scotland during the eighteenth and nineteenth centuries. In Scotland much of this lore was embodied in a 'secret' society known as The Society of the Horseman's Word, a cross between a masonic order and a trade union, in which a new member would undergo mystic initiation rites after which he was given 'The Word' which gave him power over horses.

Waggoners outside Leigh Court Barns, Worcestershire c.1900

In East Anglia horsemen sometimes earned the name of 'horse witches' from their power of 'jading' horses, that is being able to make them stand as if bewitched, and also of 'calling' or attracting horses to them. Aids to their magical power was held in the use of such things as the 'milt' (a fibrous lump found in the mouth of a new-born foal) and a frog or toad's bone. The milt was taken from the colt's mouth at birth and prepared in secret recipes, often mixing it with 'drawing oils', that would thereafter act as an allurement or charm. The toad's bone, according to Evans, was invariably used in jading horses and was indeed prepared from the pelvic bone of a toad or frog which had been cast into a flowing stream at midnight. One of the bones then floated upstream against the current and this gave its possessor 'magic' control over horses. As with the milt, the bones were sometimes powdered and mixed with scented oils. It is interesting to note that the shape of these bones are remarkably similar to the shape of the frog on the horse's hoof and one is inclined to consider the likelihood of sympathetic magic in such rituals. Evans reaches the conclusion that:

...over many years of trying to find the pattern of these so-called magical practices convinces me that there was in fact nothing magic about it at all.

Lawrence Harper, a 'toadman' was landlord of the Red Lion in Sculthorpe, Norfolk, around 1860. A well known horse dealer, he had compiled a book about horse remedies and cures and displayed remarkable powers over the control and handling of horses. On one occasion in the Red Lion Lawrence became embroiled in an argument with a rival horseman over who was best at handling horses. Lawrence demonstrated his power by going outside where his rival's horses were harnessed to a wagon. He cast a spell over them and they absolutely refused to budge until Lawrence had given the word and broken the spell.

Horse handler Edwin Hunt at Crowcombe Court in Somerset c.1900.

To end this chapter we will look a the work on the farm through a typical year, using photographs from around the late nineteenth century to the opening of the Great War, acknowledging of course that regional variations, types of soil and climate, would greatly vary the timing and methods of farming. Great variation in the use of horses in farming, the types of harness, wagons and other equipment, and even the way in which horses were trained and words of command differed county by county. Throughout this book photographs and direct quotations have been deliberately chosen across a broad range of locations in order to provide some sense of just how varied these customs and traditions were.

SPRING AND SUMMER

Preparing ground on a one-horse Dartmoor farm. Workers have taken off the turf and are raking it into piles to be burnt. The butt cart will be used to spread the resultant ash across the field while the horse is attached to the seed drill for the land to be tilled. These unique photographs were taken in 1883.

In winter farmyards were often a sea of mud and it was then that horses needed the greatest care. Here members of the Boundy family gather in the yard c.1900 to have their photograph taken alongside the newly clipped and combed workhorse.

Late spring and the ground that was ploughed in the autumn is prepared for drilling seed. This scene is at Litcham in Norfolk, taken c.1915.

Fertilising fields was a task carried out in early spring, as it had been for centuries, using materials to hand, though from the 1860s onwards the effectiveness of imported phosphates in the form of guano was recognised. Here, on a Dartmoor farm in 1886, the horse has drawn the butt cart, or dung cart, out from the farm to the fields where the workers spread it using forks. Waysoil, the earth and debris washed down into lanes from the fields, was also used as a fertiliser.

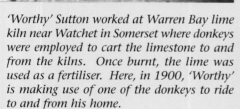

'Worthy' Sutton worked at Warren Bay lime kiln near Watchet in Somerset where donkeys were employed to cart the limestone to and from the kilns. Once burnt, the lime was used as a fertiliser. Here, in 1900, 'Worthy' is making use of one of the donkeys to ride to and from his home.

In Somerset, near Minehead, this early photograph (1875) shows a cart loaded with seaweed, also an important fertiliser, used especially on coastal farms.

Regulations and Restrictions

FOR

GOVERNING THE COMPETITION.

ART. Competitors for any of the foregoing Prizes, except in Class 13, must be workmen or servants of Subscribers of not less than 10s., and subject to all rules and regulations laid down by the Committee. No Competitors (except in Classes 4, 5, 14, and 15) will be allowed to take the same or a less Prize than they have previously taken.

COMPETITORS FOR PLOUGHING.—The name of the Plough-man, and the name of the master or mistress recommending him, and the class in which he intends to compete, must be sent to the Secretary four clear days before the day of competition. Ploughmen must be in the field with their teams ready to start at 9 o'clock in the morning.

The Agricultural Labourer, for working the longest time on the farm or farms, must send to the Secretary, on or before the 16th of October, a certificate from his master or mistress, stating his name, and the master's or mistress's name, the name of the farm or farms he has been employed upon, and the exact time the employment has been.

The Female Indoor Servant competing for length of servitude, &c., must send to the Secretary, on or before the 16th of October, a certificate from her master or mistress, stating her name, and her master's or mistress's name, the capacity in which she has been employed, and the exact time she has been in the service.

Members intending their Shepherds to compete for rearing lambs, must apply to the Secretary for a form of certificate, which must be filled up and returned to him on or before the 10th of May. No member allowed to enter in both classes without an additional subscription of 10s., and then not with the same Shepherd, or in the same parish.

Competitors in Classes 6 and 7 must have previously shorn sheep for hire for a subscriber, who will then be entitled to recommend them to compete; which must be sent to the Secretary three clear days before the day of competition.

Above: A plough team stop for a photograph at Ottery St Mary, Devon, c.1914.

Far left: Making a turn at the headland on steep land at the edge of Dartmoor. On such rocky land good voice command over the horses was vital to avoid damage to the plough or injury to the animals.

Left: Regulations for a ploughing match held at Creech St Michael, Somerset, in 1890.

Haymaking, usually carried out in May and June was work that, prior to the introduction of horse-drawn mowers and rakes, was done almost entirely by hand; the grass cut with scythes and raked into rows to dry before being taken to the rick on a hay wagon. The first horse-drawn mowers appeared in the 1820s and various types were developed, the most popular using a scissor-like action operating against a stationary bar such as the one seen in this photograph.

After cutting, the hay was tossed using a hay tedder, the operation carried out a number of times if necessary to ensure it was dry. Here Phyllis Gough is seen driving this lightweight machine pulled by a single horse. All three photographs on this page were taken at Foxworthy Farm, Devon, in 1910.

Once cut the hay was raked into windrows in order to make operations for collection more straightforward. The 'whoa-back' rake, so called because the horse had to be reversed every so often in order to dump the hay already collected, was introduced in 1825 and the dump rake in 1853. In the photograph (left) the horse is drawing the rake up a steep incline and the farmer has his hand on the mechanism used to raise the curved teeth to dump the hay.

A somewhat weary-looking horse stands at the side of a hayrick at a farm in Hewas Water, Cornwall c.1900. The boy on the horse's back has been walking backwards and forwards all day in order to lift bundles of hay from the cart up to the top of the rick using the haypole. Secured by guy ropes alongside the rick, and using a pulley block attached to the top of the pole, hay is swung up to the workers on the top of the rick using a grab, one end of which is attached by a rope to the horse's harness.

The grain harvest began in August and heralded in a busy time for the farmer, his workers and villagers, including children who were allowed time out of school to work in the fields. The two photographs above show a corn mower at work, the forerunner of the reaper-binder which combined in one operation the task of cutting and binding the shocks of corn. Above: *A two-horse team at Park Farm, Monks Orchard, c.1900.* Above right: *Men and children in the harvest fields at Woodbury, Devon, c.1904.*

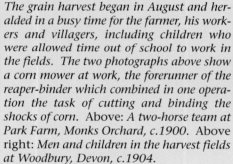

Tied shocks of corn lie alongside the three-horse sail reaper-binder at Sculthorpe in Norfolk c.1910. A man rides the leading horse while another operates the binder from a seat at the rear. Rabbits retreated to the centre of the field where the corn was yet to be cut and provided sport and food for the workers, here armed with shotguns. The child stands in front of a stook (a pyramid of stacked shocks) which would later be collected by horse and wagon to be taken to the rick.

"The Farmer's brightest prospects are now bursting upon him, and the fields are all ripening to harvest, while the wavy corn recalls the many bygone years of 'peace with plenty crowned', and the many happy harvest homes. This is indeed to the farmer the happiest and the busiest of all the months, and heaven's rich reward of industry and patience; now are the almost deserted barns opening wide their doors, waiting the treasures of the field."

Webb's *Practical Farmers' Account Book* 1900.

A three-horse teams pulls a binder up towards the brow of the hill in this superb photograph of the corn harvest taken at the evocatively named 'Golden Row' field at North Wyke in Devon on 22 August 1902.

AUTUMN AND WINTER

Above: *Building a stack at Hemblington, Norfolk in the early 1900s. The last of the grain is harvested in early September and ricks are built and thatched. In some areas stacks were built on to a base of hedge trimmings, cut by the men at the end of May, as the corn stacks were never put down on the bare ground. The long stalks of straw bearing the heads of precious grain would wait for threshing in the winter months.*

Above right: *Threshing at Pulley Mills, High Bickington, Devon in 1920. Shocks of grain are taken up into the barn from the wagon to where the threshing machine (known also as a drum) separates the grain from the stalks. The straw, expelled down the shute, is used for bedding and the grain for animal feed, for seed or for milling.*

Right: *Workers take break from threshing in the open air. Here the threshing drum sits between two stacks in order to make it easier to fork the shocks of grain into the top of the machine. The horse and cart waits to carry away the sacks of grain.*

Sacks of grain are loaded into the cart to be taken to the barn. In the background is the steam engine used to drive the threshing drum.

Potato picking at Ford Farm South Tawton, Devon c.1900. The harvested potatoes are piled at the field's edge where they will be taken in sacks to be stored. In some cases a potato clamp would be built, effectively burying the potatoes under a bank of earth to preserve them from frost and to keep them in dark and dry conditions over winter.

Above: *Winter fuel. Delivering bundles of faggots to farmworkers' cottages in Cerne Abbas c.1900.*

Carting mangolds for winter feed was one of the most onerous farm tasks for man and beast. Cold and often wet and muddy, pulling the mangolds and cutting off their leafy tops was backbreaking labour. Top: Ivybridge, Devon 1907. Right: Roadwater, Somerset c.1905.

48

At Thickthorne Farm, Hethersett, Norfolk, Mr Riches advertises the benefits of using Hadfield's Turnip Manure c.1890.

A pair of horses stand outside Church Farm, Hindringham, Norfolk in the early 1900s. Note the mud on the animals' legs and on the wheels of the tumbril. The state of the roads is a constant topic among rural diarists of the tim, with heavy rain often washing away the road surface completely.

"You cut the hay out of the rick with a hay-knife, into squares weighing about forty pounds, then you put them into this machine. They had great big weights that pulled down tight on the hay. That's what they called a hay-tier. It compressed the hay. You stored the hay into a rick first, to compress it in the first place, then it'd be cut and done by a hay-tier for transportation for sale. The canal used to take the hay for the horses that draw the barge. But then of course balers came along and took over from hay-tiers."

*Hay tiers with their loads of hay outside the
Red Lion inn at Woolmer Green c.1900.*

50

The Horse and the Village

While village and farming life went hand in hand there were, as far as the use and care of the horse was concerned, a number of distinct occupations and events that generally centred upon the community. Indeed most farmworkers would be housed in cottages that were themselves part of the village and, although the poorer labourers would not own horses themselves, their work with horses would bring them through the village almost daily. In this chapter we consider the late Victorian and Edwardian village scene, before the era when motor vehicles began to take over from horse-drawn carriages, when the sound of the blacksmith's hammer rang like a bell chiming the slow hours away.

The ownership of a horse remained well beyond the purse of most villagers, not only in the price of purchasing an animal but in the costs of upkeep and in providing suitable stabling. It was hard enough for poorly paid agricultural workers and other labourers to feed their families without the further expense of maintaining a horse or pony, unless directly associated with their work.

A tranquil village scene in Elmsett c.1910 with a horse-drawn gig waiting outside the Rose & Crown inn.

GOODBYE OLD FRIEND

THE BLACKSMITH

The archetypal image of the village blacksmith, leather apron and hammer in hand, standing larger than life outside the smithy is borne out by contemporary photographs and descriptions. Historically the blacksmith's trade goes back into prehistory, to the legend of Wayland Smith and to the age when the transmutation of metals was an alchemic art. Even in the period in which the dying light of their fires was upon them, the village smith retained a presence of some mystery to the village children, as Alison Uttley recalls in her book *Country Hoard*:

The village blacksmiths and their families stand outside the smithy in Grampound, Cornwall c.1900. The metal disk on the floor in front of the men is a wheelbinding plate used when shrinking the hot metal rims on to wagon wheels.

The strange smells of the smith attracted me, and I stood as near the open door as I dared. The blacksmith was a morose man, in his leathern apron, dark and torn. His face was dark, his hair coal black, his temper was irritable, he shouted strange oaths and threw down his hammer with such a clatter it was like doom. He blew up the fire with wheezing bellows, and a shower of golden sparks went through the hole in the roof to the trees above.

A classic photograph of a blacksmith shoeing a grey horse at South Tawton in Devon c.1910.

While in the popular imagination the blacksmith's job centred on the shoeing of horses, in fact his principal occupation lay in the working of metal which might include 'the blades for the harrows, the share and coulters for the ploughs, the shoes for the oxen and horses and nails and bolts'. He even made the iron hoops and crooks for the children's game of 'bowling'. He was often a jack of all trades, particularly in the absence of specialist farriers and wheelwrights, and the smithy itself provided a convenient centre for villagers to gather, and even to experience some rudimentary dental work:

Locks Green smithy was one of the warmest places in the district, especially in winter, so the blacksmith, Fred Heal, was rarely short of company. The 'village parliament' met here, and villagers relaxed here after work. At the end of each day neighbours and workmen gathered to swap their stories and tell their yarns whilst sharing a 'plug o' baccy', playing a game of 'Tippit', or watching villagers have their teeth pulled!

Robert Thrower, blacksmith at Strumpshaw in Norfolk, with two of his children, July 1884. The 1841 census shows over 97 000 blacksmiths employed in Britain, of which around 500 were women.

Above right: *The interior of Howard's Smithy in Bakewell, Derbyshire c.1910. The smith on the right is working the bellows on the forge while his colleague has two horses to shoe.*

Above: *Blacksmith Jack Thorne and his apprentices making horse-shoes on an anvil outside the smithy in Pimperne, Dorset.*

Right: *Fred Heal shoes a horse at the smithy in Locks Green on the Isle of Wight c.1910. There are two sets of harrows and various iron rims of wagon wheels leaning against the wall indicating the general work undertaken by the blacksmith. Note also the stone trough behind the horse and the grindstone far left, all part of the smith's trade.*

THE WHEELWRIGHT

Smoke and steam fill the air outside the smithy in Swanage in the late 1890s as a new iron tyre is set on to the rim of a wagon wheel.

While the village blacksmith could be called upon to repair and reshod wagon wheels, the art of making a wheel itself was a specialism of the wheelwright who sometimes also produced wagon bodies of various types, as George Sturt describes in his book *The Wheelwright's Shop* published in 1923: 'The complete wheelwright, acquiring skill of hands to make a wheel, was a good enough workman then for the job of building a wagon throughout and painting it too.' But by that date the occupation was in terminal decline, the number of wheelwrights falling by almost 20 per cent between 1901, when 29 000 were employed in Great Britain, to under 24 000 in 1911.

The component parts of a spoked wheel: hub, fellows, spokes, and so on, required specific seasoned timber if they were to live up to the hard work expected of them, and specialist tools to fashion them. The wheelwright's shop, like the smithy, was a busy centre of activity in the village. As a skilled carpenter the wheelwright might also be called upon to make coffins (often the village wheelwright also doubled as the undertaker), yokes for the oxen, horses and donkeys, handles for scythes and reap hooks, the frames for the winnowing-fans and harrows, the seedlips for the sowing, and wooden rakes.

James Parker Mitchell, wheelwright of Litcham in Norfolk, c.1900.

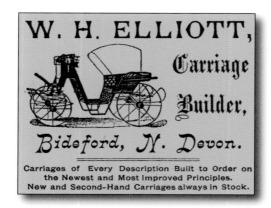

THE CARRIAGEMAKER AND WAINWRIGHT

Farm wagons were constructed along the same lines as small vessels, using traditional carpentry skills that had survived for centuries. Some of the finest of these, now preserved in museums, are approaching two hundred years in age. Each was built for a specific task on the farm, with regional variations employed to suit both the terrain and local taste. Magnificent hay wagons, brightly painted, celebrated the skills of both wainwrighting and wheelwrighting, with something of the blacksmith's art thrown in. Two-wheeled dung carts, or butt carts as they were known in other regions, were among the most functional farm vehicles, drab and robust.

Respective carriagemakers, like car manufacturers today, built vehicles that ranged from the everyday runabout to prestige models of the highest quality, bringing in the skills of the upholsterer and harnessmaker to complete the most luxurious and expensive carriages. While the most ancient dogcart might serve a poor farmer, exotic carriages would emerge from the gates of the landed gentry's country seat, a conveyance for every eventuality and bearing such names as barouche, brougham, landau, phaeton, stanhope and sulky, to be used as fashion dictated.

A handsome hay cart stands at the back of the dairy cottages at Coker's Frome in Dorset in 1890. A tranquil scene reflected in the pond in the foreground.

Above left: Wheelwright and carriage builder Robert Harvey of West Coker stands beside a newly completed wagon made for the Dawes Twine Works c.1890.

Above: The first page of Articles of Indenture of 15 year old Thomas Andrew as a wheelwright's apprentice at Northlew in Devon in 1875. The young Thomas foreswore fornication, marriage and gambling throughout his 5 years as apprentice, during which he would be paid nothing for the first two years, £1 in the third year, £2 in the fourth year and £3 in his final year.

Left: A dogcart made by Thomas Andrew at Northlew c.1910, some 30 years after he completed his apprenticeship.

Right: *Coachbuilder, wheelwright and undertaker, W. Ward stands with his family and apprentices outside his workshop in St Ives, Cornwall c.1890. Note the farm wagon on the right and the two delivery carts on the left, one for the local butcher and the other for the baker.*

Below: *William Edward Jory with his dog Carlo sitting in the newly made dogcart outside his workshop in Kingskerswell, Devon c.1910.*

Above: *Workers at Hicks' carriage works, Truro. In 1876 Samuel Hicks took over the business and he is seen here in the centre of the picture wearing the bowler hat.*

Right: *Employees at Moor's Yard carriage works, South Molton in Devon c.1890.*

The house and workshop of Banner & Sons at Leigh Sinton in Worcestershire c.1900. The sign above the workshop door advertises their expertise as practical coach builders, carpenters, and coffin makers.

THE SADDLER AND HARNESSMAKER

In 1841 there were 15 723 people occupied as saddlers and harnessmakers in Great Britain, a figure that increased to over 16 500 by 1881, and which continued to rise, almost doubling in number by 1901. In the years immediately before the First World War work in this field dwindled in rural areas, with those skilled in working with leather migrating to the cities to work, manufacturing leather good such as trunks and upholstery for motor vehicles. Many moved farther afield as the daughter of Edgar Dyer of Dunster recalls:

On leaving school my father was apprenticed to the saddlery trade and served his apprenticeship at Ernest Norman's main shop in North Street, Taunton. When my father completed his apprenticeship, work was hard to find so in 1912 he and a number of lads from Dunster and the surrounding district emigrated to Canada to seek work.

Much of the harnessmaker's work would be in repairing broken and damaged gear, but many of those working in leather would also be in the boot and shoe business.

The workmen's boots were all of very hard and heavy leather, shod with steel all around the edges and with many studs underneath. When I received my first pair I was so proud of my personal footprint that I left in the drying mud, my father having specially designed the pattern the studs should form.

ESTABLISHED 1764.

FRANK T. LONG,
BUILDER, UNDERTAKER & WHEELWRIGHT.

LIGHT SPRING CARTS AND VANS
BUILT TO ORDER.

FIELD GATES AND HURDLES SUPPLIED.
PRICES ON APPLICATION.

OPPOSITE THE "SUN INN," CALBOURNE,
ISLE OF WIGHT.

JOHN GUSTAR,
Builder & Contractor, Wheelwright
AND
UNDERTAKER,
CALBOURNE, ISLE OF WIGHT.

LIGHT OR HEAVY WAGGONS BUILT TO ORDER.
Estimates for Repairs. Prompt & careful attention to all orders.

ROBERT PHILLIPS,
HARNESS MAKER, SADDLER,
AND
BOOT AND SHOE MAKER,
CALBOURNE.
All Orders Carefully executed. Postal Communications promptly
attended to. ESTABLISHED 50 YEARS.

WALTER NEAT, Ironmonger, Basket, Mat, Brush, and
Lamp Oil Dealer, visits Calbourne on Mondays.

An advertisement from Pike's Directory of 1881 including Robert Phillips, harnessmaker, saddler and boot and shoe maker.

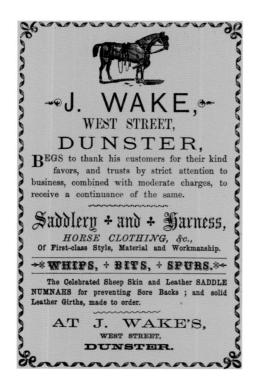

On show days and at fairs the harnessmaker's craft would be shown off to its very best in the gleaming leather and bright brasses adorning the farmers' horses. The making of headcollars, martingales, bridles, stallion rollers, plough gear and other parts of a working horse's equipment required a long apprenticeship, usually seven years. For much of the metalwork used in harness gear, and in connecting the working horse to a plough or wagon, the harness maker would look to the local blacksmith, especially where repairs were required.

Celebrated collector of rural voices from the past, Mollie Harris, in her book *From Acre End*, records the memories of Harold Quanton, son of an Oxfordshire harness-maker of the late nineteenth century:

Father would work very hard in those days with only a pushbike to get around on. Few farmers would deliver and fetch their repaired harness, and he had to cycle to them to fetch the harness, including collars and saddles. He had a way of loading his bike with two collars hanging each side from a carrier over the back wheel, and usually a saddle on top and smaller pieces of harness on the handlebars... Father had large white leather hides hung up in his shop from which he made hedging cuffs, thongs for the farm carters' boots, and heavy stitching leather for horse collars and saddles etc. For stitching he used large curved needles with a steel palm tool.

Sydney Ashman and his assistants outside the saddlery at Thatcham, Berkshire c.1910.

Above: *The harnessmaker's workshop of H. Pryke in Haughly c.1900.*

Above left: *Stone's saddlers and harness-makers in Mere, Somerset. The display was to celebrate King Edward II's coronation in 1902.* Below: *A horse brass made to celebrate the coronation.*

Right: *Hickling's harnessmaker's shop in Hethersett, Norfolk, c.1908. Note the dilap-idated horse collars standing against the wall waiting for repairs.*

GOODBYE OLD FRIEND

THE ROUNDSMAN

In earlier centuries villages were self contained as far as provisions were concerned. Most of what the villager required was found locally, or purchased at the local market. Itinerant travellers and tinkers might appear from time to time, carrying with them small trinkets, ribbons and other knick knacks. As Queen Victoria's reign progressed and the web of railways spread across the country carrying milk and other farm produce daily to the cities, more and more items became available to country dwellers too. Out from nearby towns and neighbouring villages came the roundsmen with their horses and carts of various types, appearing at set intervals with goods and services that hitherto were rarely seen in the deeper parts of the countryside. An article in *The Times* describes the pattern of the roundsmen life on Dartmoor in the early 1900s:

Billy Lambert and Bob Hall in Sheringham. Norfolk, pose for the camera on their daily bread delivery round c.1910.

The Dartmoor cottager and farmer on the southern slopes of the moor looked for his household supplies to the itinerant roundsman who came out once a month from Ashburton or Buckfastleigh loaded up with oil, candles, soap, pots and pans. The wagon

62

was a heavy load for Bob the horse, but he knew the roads as well as the roundsman and took to the hills with professional slowness and certainty. On the long pull up towards Poundsgate and Holne I used to walk behind the wagon ready to slip the iron shoe under one of the back wheels to give Bob a rest. He knew exactly where to stop.

The roundsman I adventured with as a schoolboy had a long, open four-wheeled wagon packed with his stock hidden beneath an old tarpaulin. Built into the back of the wagon was a big square oil drum with a large tap, and to work the tap you needed a special spanner-screw which the roundsman kept secretively in his oily jacket pocket. Everything smelt of oil. Even though oil was only a penny a pint it was a profitable business, and made the long trek on the moor worth while.

He never pressed people to buy, but the big, oily pocket book helped to make it easy, for, with 'Plymouth orders', he accepted advanced payments of 6d a week. Rolls and rolls of linoleum decorated with roses and lilies went into those Dartmoor cottages. The lino's pungent smell of linseed oil and glue filled the cottage when we dumped the roll inside the door. We sold soap by the yard. It was coarse red and yellow stuff. Only occasionally would a cottager break out into a tablet of the new fancy toilet soap to go with the soap dish in the toilet set. Soda was shovelled out of a sack into a brown stone jar which every cottage had in the back of the kitchen. Candles were another permanent

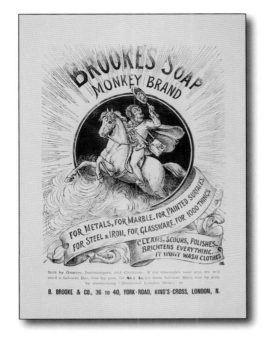

Along with the daily necessities, roundsmen made the most of the Victorians' obsessions with cleanliness, the ideal mother and wife being easily persuaded to invest in the latest soaps, polishes and grate-blacking.

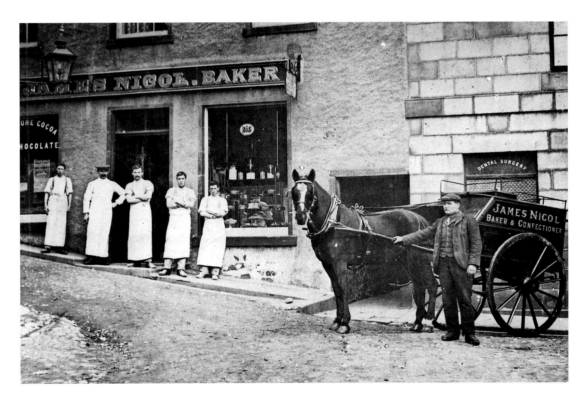

James Nicol, Banff's baker and his assistants pose outside the shop with the horse and delivery cart c.1900.

stock in trade, and you could get a twopenny candlestick made of tin. Night lights were popular too because they burned very slowly and there were small ones for a halfpenny. The Dartmoor purchaser had to watch his farthings and ha'pennies against the day when perhaps a new kettle was needed which might run to two shillings.

The roundsman's kettles were famous – made with vast double-block tin bottoms capable of riding the most mountainous wood fire, or enduring the heat of a whole winter of peat firing. In fact the roundsman's whole day on the moor was concerned with maintaining warmth and cleanliness.

Palmers' bakery van at Haughley, Suffolk c.1914.

Above: *Bazley's delivery van in Bridport, Dorset in 1910. The canvas hood advertises ironmongery, bedsteads, bedding, furniture, earthenware and china.*

Above left: *'Skipper' delivered bread and groceries in and around Wendling in Norfolk at the turn of the nineteenth century.*

BREAD

Above: *'Tommy' the horse waits patiently with the bread cart outside the Seven Stars Inn, Kingskerswell in Devon in 1909.*

Above right: *Fred and William Lusher delivering bread around Bodham, Norfolk.*

WATER

Today we take the provision of water for granted. It was not always so easily obtainable for the Victorians, and even into the twentieth century rural areas were faced with intermittent supplies, especially in dry summers.

Left: Municipal water companies flourished in the nineteenth century, providing water to towns and villages through integrated systems of supply. Here we see employees of the Sheringham Gas and Water Company with their cart around 1905.

Below left: As late as the 1950s the villagers of Priddy in Somerset had no constant supply of water. Here we see a line of horses and carts with various containers queueing to draw water from a fountain in front of Fountain Cottage c.1920.

Below: 'Blind David' Annear with his boy helper, delivers water in a bucket to Mary Hensley in St Day, Cornwall in the 1920s.

MEAT

Clockwise from top left: *Delivery boy outside Codd the butcher's shop in 1913. Note the ubiquitous wicker basket used by both butchers and bakers; Delivery boy on horse and pony and cart pose outside the Swan Inn, Alfrick, Worcestershire.1920; The butcher with his striped apron outside the village shop in Cerne Abbas c.1920; Delivery cart, the butcher and assistants stand outside Glover's in Bideford, Devon c.1910.*

MILK

Some villagers kept a dairy cow, others relied on the local farmer to provide milk which was then made into butter, clotted cream and cheese. The development of the railway network from the mid 1800s meant that milk could be taken daily from remote parts of the countryside into the cities, and from this grew, in the mid twentieth century, a huge network of dairies and transport companies dedicated to the doorstep delivery of the daily pint. In rural parts of Victorian and Edwardian Britain milk was collected daily from farms in churns and distributed throughout the community by enterprising individuals or by small dairies which processed the milk, providing other dairy produce too.

Left: *Sheringham Hall Dairy milk float, Norfolk, early 1900s. Note the distinctive shape of the churns in the cart, and the cans which the men are carrying into which the milk was decanted. Each man carries pint and half pint measures which would be used on the doorstep to fill the householder's jug.*

Above: *Ernie Worth leads 'Robin' and the milk cart delivering milk from Peat Cott Farm on Dartmoor to Princetown c.1920.*

Left: *Hester Larke in the Hellesdon Dairy milk cart, Norfolk c.1918.*

69

FISH

As with all perishable items, their timely distribution was critical, nothing more so than with fish. Before the railways the supply of fresh fish was limited to those communities living nears coasts and rivers.

Above: Tom 'Crackpot' Craske of Sheringham in Norfolk stands with his donkey and cart from which he sold fish locally around 1900. Painted on the side of the cart (by a dyslexic signwriter?) are the words 'Fish Daler'.

Above right: Another eccentric is George 'Pegleg' Onions of Shaldon in Devon, who sold fish and shellfish from his cart to the villages along the banks of the River Teign in the early 1900s.

Right: In Cornwall fish sellers were known as jowsters, or jousters, and the arrival of this man (holding up a fish) and his horse and cart has coincided with a general gathering of the population of Crowlas, near Penzance, in the late 1800s.

COACHES

For centuries before the coming of the railway the stage coach had provided the principal means by which travellers could move in relative comfort over long distances. Staging posts, where the horses could be changed and the passengers fed, grew up as coaching inns in towns along the major routes which were also followed by passenger-carrying mail coaches. Roads were notoriously bad and sometimes impassable in the winter months, but the development of turnpikes improved this somewhat and by the mid Victorian period travel by this means had reached its peak of comfort and efficiency, only to be swept aside by the speed and convenience of the railway. By the early 1900s the last of these long-distance coaches had disappeared. What remained were horse-drawn charabancs, coaches and horse buses which followed local routes and ferried passengers on day trips, and to and from towns and railway stations.

In more remote parts of the country local horse-drawn coaches survived well into the early years of the twentieth century. Here a crowded coach leaves Minehead station heading for Lynton and Lynmouth c.1905.

Horse bus 'Victoria' that carried passengers between Penzance and Land's End in the early 1900s.

A mail coach timetable running between Derby and Manchester in 1840. In the left hand column are the hours allowed for each section of the journey and in the right hand column the driver was obliged to write in the actual time taken.

Opposite page: *Carrier Edwin Holbrook at Locks Green on the Isle of Wight in 1904.*

In *Small Talk at Wreyland* Cecil Torr refers to his father's Devon diaries concerning the discomfort and perils of coach travel:

Travelling by coach was not so very much better than on horseback. In his diary dated Friday 5th February 1836, my father notes: 'snow up the country, so that the Tuesday coaches could not come in until Thursday'. Writing to him from London after a journey up, 7th April 1839, an old friend of his exclaims: 'Oh that Salisbury Plain, thirty-five miles of a wet windy night outside a coach, by God, sir, tis no joke."

The same friend writes to him from Sidmouth, 11th January 1841, after coming from Southampton to Honiton by coach: 'We had six horses nearly all the way, and soon after passing Ringwood, our road was covered with snow which was a least four feet deep on either side. We got capsized into a high bank on descending one hill, but it was managed so very quietly that we were not thrown off.'

On the London and Exeter coaches the tips came to about a quarter of the fare: one to the guard, three to the drivers (drivers being changed at the supper and breakfast stops) and two to the ostlers at each end.

On 14th July 1839 my father write to my grandfather that railway fares are comparatively low and no fees apply, that is tips.

THE CARRIER

My life began on the carrier's cart which brought me up the long slow hills to the village, and dumped me in the high grass, and lost me. I had ridden wrapped up in a Union Jack to protect me from the sun, and when I rolled out of it, and stood piping loud among the buzzing jungle of that summer bank, then, I feel, was I born.

Laurie Lee's experience of the carrier as described in *Cider With Rosie* would not have been unusual in the years before motors and railways, for the carrier was the main means of transportation for the rural poor and their goods. Sometimes farmers took on the role of carrying other people's as well as their own goods to weekly markets, and the carriers

W. Pridham & Son

Established 1812

Carriers, Removers, and Storers of Household Furniture, etc.

Delivery Agents to the L. & S.W. Railway.

Separate Lock-up Dry Rooms for Storing Furniture, Luggage, etc., at Moderate Rents.

ESTIMATES FREE

HOUSEHOLD REMOVALS

W. PRIDHAM & SON

TO ALL PARTS

All kinds of Packing done by Experienced Packers. Piano and other Cases and Mats supplied.

Delivery Vans to Northam, Westward Ho! and Appledore daily, from the Goods and Passenger Stations.

Steamship Passenger Agents.

Parcels, Goods, Baggage, etc., shipped to all parts abroad by the Principal Lines.

OFFICE— **Broad Quay.**

E. HOLBROOK, CARRIER, PORCHFIELD.

A very early photograph of a carrier's cart in Dunster High Street, 1875.

William Rice (1852–1933) who was born at Cheriton Bishop in Devon and worked all his life as a carter and carrier. It was said that he could take his horse and cart from Lustleigh to Exeter and back in a day, a distance of 35 miles.

themselves would often have some other form of trade. On busier thoroughfares those wishing to use the carrier's services would hang out a flag or some other sign so that the carrier would know they wanted to ride with him or had goods to be delivered.

Unlike the roundsmen whose job it was to deliver goods on a daily round within a small area, carriers and their carts went wherever they were paid to go. If called upon to carry goods over long distances they would relay them from place to place, or transfer them to the nearest railway depot if that was more convenient. Cecil Torr records that his grandfather used the services of carriers taking some valuables from Lustleigh in Devon to London:

There are letters of 13 and 17 August 1843 about some forks and spoons and other silver things that he was sending to my father: they have been packed into a carpet bag, and this being rolled up in the middle of two feather beds, and the package will be sent by carrier's wagon. 'How long it will be going up, I am not aware.' It was sent to More-ton, and one carrier to it on to Exeter, another to Wellington, and so on.

That the items had to be concealed is perhaps some indication of the vulnerability of transporting goods over long distances on a journey that could take many days. The railway to Lustleigh did not open until 1866 and Torr records that in 1913 he brought the same goods back to Devon on the train in just five hours.

Eventually the carriers appear to have settled upon a general type of wagon that in some respects resembled the covered wagons used by the settlers of North America, the hooped canvas cover affording some protection to both passengers and goods. The carriers themselves were, by law, obliged to walk alongside the horses in order to maintain control of them and thus prevent accidents. These wagons were the fore-runners of the horse bus and eventually set timetables began to appear stating that such-and-such a wagon would be leaving, often from the local inn, at a specified time.

As the railway network reached farther into the more remote parts of Britain so the carrier became the prime link between the railway station and the customer. They were the 'white van man' equivalent of their day. Increasingly the railway companies formed their own horse-drawn transport links, ferrying goods and people to and from their stations.

Coal merchant and carrier Richard Passmore from Okehampton became delivery agent for the London & South Western Railway in 1879.

Recognising the lucrative trade in carrying goods and passengers to and from their stations, railway companies began rapidly expanding their own fleet of carts and buses. Here is an early example of a horse bus belonging to the Bristol & Exeter Railway Company outside the Railway Hotel, Bridgwater in 1865.

Below: A Royal Mail horse bus entering Penzance c.1910. A horse omnibus, operated by Archelaus Thomas of St Just, continued in service carrying the Royal Mail from that area of Penzance up to the end of 1920. This was sixteen years after motor transport buses had begun to run a service to the town, as he still retained the Post Office contract. A Mr Brendon of Bude operated another of the last horse-drawn vehicles in the county to carry the Royal Mail, up until 1919.

The Mail Carrier

In 1719 Ralph Allen, Postmaster at Bath, signed the first of a number of contracts with the Post Office to develop and expand Britain's postal network. He organised mail coaches which were to become the principal means of transporting letters between Britain's major cities, the first regular mail coach service running between Bristol and London in 1784. By the 1830s came the first use of the railway to carry letters, and in 1846 the last horse-drawn mail coach left London for Norwich, although a long-distance service was reopened in 1887 for the carriage of parcels. These early Royal Mail coaches bore Royal Mail livery and the Royal Cipher.

In 1840 Rowland Hill introduced the penny post and it became possible to send and receive a letter anywhere in Great Britain and Ireland, pre-paid by the sender. By the late nineteenth century there were between six and twelve mail deliveries per day in London, but in rural areas the service was less secure and letters could take some days to reach their destination, especially if the roads were made impassable during bad weather. This rural service was originally provided via the carrier's cart who picked up bags of mail from the nearest town and delivered them to a designated village postman. Known as a 'sub-postmaster', these individuals were often simply

Above left: *Torquay mail coach 1915. The Drake family held the contract with the Post Office for 'the conveyance of mail' between Torquay Post Office and the railway station.*

Above: *Mail was carried between St Dennis and St Austell in Cornwall by a uniformed postman in a pony and trap c.1910.*

Left: *The postman's cart waits outside the Post Office, Beaminster, Dorset c.1900.*

supplementing their income with this part-time job, working from their own homes. Eventually the service became regularised, with full time postmen and women working in village post offices which received and franked their own mail. From 1890 onwards pillar boxes began to appear in most towns and villages.

While many rural postmen delivered and picked up mail on horseback the arrival of the bicycle began to challenge horse power and in 1897 the Post Office officially introduced the use of cycles.

The Village Inn

In the Victorian period village inns served as a central meeting point, and often as an overnight stopping place for travellers. In some places the pubs brewed their own beer but this was becoming less common as larger brewers, centred in towns, took over most of this trade, supplying the inns in their area via regular deliveries. The brewer's dray was a familiar sight both in town and country. Ever conscious of their propriety, the middle classes looked upon the common hostelry as places of iniquity and generally shunned them. As the railways flourished so did public houses, and railway hotels sprang up next to railway stations across the country. These served as

Above: Bicycles officially began to replace horse power in mail deliveries from 1897 as the increase in telegram traffic grew.

A brewer's dray delivering barrels of beer to the White Lion Inn, Bridgwater in Somerset, 1865.

convenient transit points for the growing numbers of people who began to take holidays or weekend sightseeing trips, and new opportunities arose for the operation of horse-drawn charabancs and horse buses taking parties out to enjoy the country-side. Dorset author H.S. Joyce recalls the Edwardian village of his youth:

A horse and cart loaded with beer stands with the boy and his fellow workers outside the brewery in Stogumber, Somerset, early 1900s.

There was one public house in the village and another, which called itself a hotel, opposite the railway station... The public house stood exactly opposite the church gate and did a reasonable trade with the villagers in beer and tobacco. Sometimes a shooting or fishing party would call for a bread and cheese lunch. They were always given a little room at the back. No respectable person outside the working class ever entered the bar; it was one of those things that was not done. 'Going into pubs' was not the thing that a man would do who valued the respect of his neighbours... If he wanted a drink he sat on his horse or remained in his gig and the drink was brought out to him.

Above: *Publicans were quick to pick up on the popularity of tourists visiting the countryside wishing to hire carriages.*

Right: *Delivery to the Lobster Inn Sheringham c.1904. The cart belongs to the Midland & Northern Joint Railway Co. Note also the sign advertising pony and traps for hire, and stabling.*

Above: *Greengrocery delivery to the Ship Inn, Porlock, Somerset 1912.*

Right: *Biden brewery delivery to the Yew Tree Inn, Stoke Village, Hayling c.1910.*

EVENTS AND ENTERTAINMENTS

For many of those who lived in remote rural parts of Britain, even at the end of Victoria's reign, their world was encompassed by how far they might walk in a day. Depending upon the distance to the nearest town, a special event or market day might occasion a journey in the carrier's cart but there was otherwise little incentive to travel beyond the parish boundaries. Railways, when they arrived, were more often criticised for the number of people they brought in, than praised for the opportunities they gave the locals for travel, as Cecil Torr records:

> *This was a secluded place until the railway came. My grandfather writes on 3 January 1864, 'I cannot fancy that any railway improves scenery, but this will not so disturb it as one might imagine. They fancy it is cutting up the country and letting in more people, which will destroy the scenery and the quiet of the neighbourhood; but they think more of its introducing new society than destroying the scenery.'*

The invention of the bicycle was famously said by Laurie Lee to have reduced the incidence of incest in rural areas 'where the roads were good', and indeed for the first time the cycle opened up the possibility of travelling respectable distances in the course of a day. But country people were inured to staying put and thus any unusual

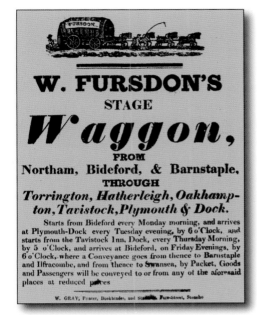

Speed was not of the essence to nineteenth century rural dwellers, the pace of life geared to the pace of the horse. Fursdon's stage waggon averaged around 2.5 miles an hour on its meandering journey across Devon.

A dapper young gent goes visiting on his bicycle near Beaminster, Dorset in 1906.

occurrence or visitation caused something of a stir. Some of these visitors appeared regularly depending upon the time of year. Itinerant workers followed the seasons of planting and harvesting, and bands of gypsies, following their own wandering stars, painted horses towing bright caravans, were not always welcome when they arrived:

We used to see many more gypsies than we do today. I remember women who would reluctantly buy sprigs of heather or clothes pegs rather than incur the displeasure or anger of the caller. It was surprising the number of people who were scared of gypsies because of the belief that if offended the gypsy would lay some terrible curse on you.

Hawkers, and those offering services such as umbrella repairs and knife and scissor sharpening would bring women and children out into the street:

I remember particularly the man we called China Dickinson who lived near Blandford Railway Station with his horse and cart, who sold china, pots and pans and paraffin. The rattle and noise of his cart could be heard from a great distance especially on his journey home in the early evening, the tin pans hitting together. He wore a waistcoat

Strawberry pickers in the fields near Swanwick, Hampshire, 1910. The horse and cart stands by ready to take the baskets of fruit to the railway station, seen in the background.

An itinerant knife grinder and the young girl have arrived at this spot in Cornwall in the 1890s. Their tent stands in the background while his horse, detached from the cart in which they travel, grazes nearby.

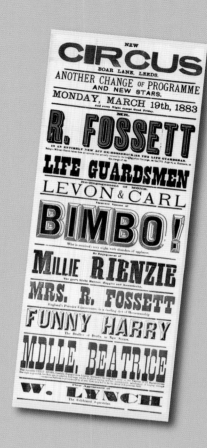

Top: *Horse-drawn wagons of a travelling fair arrive in Shaldon, Devon in 1896, featuring sideshows including 'Dooner's Amazing Rifle Range' and the 'African Jungle from the Olympia'.* Above: *The Church Army's travelling van arrives in High Bickington c.1910.* Right: *The Big Top rolls into Lydford.*

Bill Sherrin's pony stands patiently in the shafts of his rag and bone cart in the village of Carhampton in 1912. Bill also purchased rabbit skins which were used for trimmings on hats, gloves and coats.

with many buttons. As a sideline China Dickinson bought rabbit skins, paying two pence each, wild rabbits being the most common meal for country-dwellers as the countryside was heavily populated with rabbits.

Other visitors provided entertainments of one sort or another, with travelling groups of players, circuses and fairs with horse-drawn caravans making their way from village to village, stopping by tradition each year, or where they might feel there was some money to be made, and often treated with some suspicion by the locals.

Non-conformist religious groups of several denominations came seeking to evangelise the rural population – the late Victorians being particularly partial to this kind of itinerant missioning. Horse-drawn caravans acted as mobile pulpits from which earnest young preachers addressed the community. Likewise Teetotalism, a movement begun in the early nineteenth century, swept from the cities out into the countryside where huge temperance meetings were sometimes held.

*   *   *

As Victoria's reign entered its final decades, the migration of rural people to the cities, the growth of the railways, the improvement to roads and even the humble bicycle, began to erode the centuries-old dominance of the horse in Britain's countryside. But it was the steam engine that now shook the foundations of that quiet world.

Iron Horse

The potential of steam power has been recognised since Classical times and it was more a question of developing metal technology sufficient to harness it, and the imperative of a sufficient necessity for its use, that delayed progress. Requirement and technology came together in the late eighteenth century at the dawn of the Industrial Revolution, first in mining where the requirement was to drain water from deep coal mines, and later in the cotton mills and steel works. Mine engines were stationary, using vacuum to operate the rise and fall of huge pump beams. When this power was then converted to rotary motion, such engines could drive a series of machines through a system of pulleys

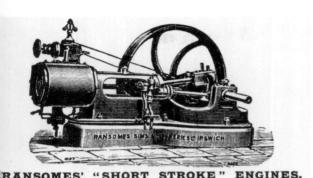

RANSOMES' "SHORT STROKE" ENGINES.

Below: A horse-drawn steam engine made by Robert Robey of Lincoln who began manufacturing portable engines in 1854. Note the water tank on the right and the lumps of coal on the floor beneath the furnace door, fuel that made working these machines expensive. Note also the large number of men required to carry out the threshing operation at this time c.1900.

and shafts. In 1801 Richard Trevithick demonstrated that steam could move a vehicle along a road, and by 1825 the first steam railway was opened.

Steam's appearance in agriculture came more slowly. Small stationary engines such as those made by Ransomes were used to operate drainage pumps, grist mills, chaff cutters and the like, but their high cost restricted their use to the wealthiest and more progressive farms. It was the weight of early steam engines that made them impractical for farm use, this and the expense of obtaining suitable fuel, and it was not until the 1850s that the first steam plough was used. Initially, then, these engines posed little threat to the horse. Indeed, the early machines were not self-propelled and required teams of horses to haul them from farm to farm.

Communities found many objections to the imposition of these engines and in rural England there remained a sceptical, often hostile, reaction to them. The heat generated at the time on both sides of the pro-horse, pro-machine debate should not be underestimated and its outcome, ultimately falling on the side of the machine, can be seen as a tipping point from which the reign of horse power is first challenged, and later toppled.

In 1831 a Parliamentary Select Committee reported on Steam Carriages, looking in particular at the imposition of tolls on turnpike roads, their safety with regard to boiler explosions, and the nuisance caused to other road users, not least to those using horses. On the matter of safety one witness refutes the suggested dangers of steam:

The danger of explosion is less than the dangers attendant on the use of horses in draught... The danger arising to passengers from the breaking of machinery, need scarcely be taken into consideration. It is a mere question of delay, and can scarcely exceed in frequency the casualties which may occur with horses.

On the question of the noise created by the machines frightening horses:

The committee believe that these statements are unfounded. Whatever noise may be complained of, arises from the present defective construction of the machinery, and will

Below: *Horse meets steam engine in East Anglia, early 1900s. The traction engine is towing a threshing set which comprises the engine itself towing a threshing drum, to which is hitched a trailer carrying fuel and the water tank. It is said that engineer Thomas Aveling, who first produced a steam plough in 1856, chose as his company emblem a rampant horse in recognition of the complaints made about steam engines frightening horses!*

While the government much earlier found favour with the introduction of steam power on the roads, people continued to be reminded of the inherent dangers of working with these machines. Top: *An overturned steam engine lies at the foot of Staunch Hill in Somerset where it had run away and crashed in 1906.* Above right: *The cataclysmic result of a boiler explosion of a ploughing engine.* Above: *A steam roller crash in Bideford in 1910 attracts a sizeable crowd, and a photographer.*

be corrected as the makers of such carriages gain greater experience. Admitting even that the present engines do work with some noise, the effects on horses has been greatly exaggerated. All the witnesses accustomed to travel in these carriages even on crowded roads... have stated that horses are very seldom frightened in passing.

The Committee concluded:

These enquiries have led the Committee that the substitution of inanimate for animal power, in draft on common roads, is one of the most important improvements in the means of internal communication ever introduced.

And for the centuries-old rule of horse power, the writing was on the wall.

Another common complaint against these new monsters was that they broke up the roads, making it difficult for other travellers. This was supposedly due to their enormous weight, some weighing as much as 20 tons (the average from 3 to 5 tons), and their ridged metal wheels. To give evidence on this aspect of the steam engine's effects on road surfaces the committee called upon the celebrated Scottish engineer Thomas Telford, the 'Colossus of Roads'. Asked what he thought most damaging, the passage of horses or the engine, he replies:

HALBERTON ROAD, TIVERTON.

By the horses chiefly, by tearing up the surface with their shoes. I do not consider the pressure of the wheels upon a good made road is nearly so injurious to the road as the tearing up of the road by the horses feet.

Indeed, while the establishment of turnpikes from the early 1700s had greatly improved the condition of Britain's roads, those in rural areas remained poor and subject to constant washing away by heavy rainfall. Ironically, though steam engines imposed dangers both to the road user, the road itself, and to culverts and bridges, it was ultimately their introduction which led to the resurfacing of all roads in the country in a uniform way. Horse transport, by its nature limited the distances to which road building material could be transported, the horses themselves, as Telford witnesses, creating damage along the way. Steam engines on the other hand could transport many tons of roadstone over much greater distances, and heavy steam rollers provided the compaction that hitherto had been impossible.

Horses and carts and pedestrians on the toll road running out of Tiverton in the 1880s. The road surface is typical of that time and represents what most rural highways looked like, compressed earth that quickly turned to mud in winter. Traffic of all kinds were subject to pay a toll when passing through the gate and the Locomotive Act of 1861 made law the tolls applicable to steam carriages.

ROAD BUILDING

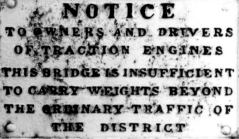

Above left: *Stone cracking at Rattery, Devon, in order to make roadstone, c.1890. Above: Workers in a Norfolk gravel pit in 1900, cast stones through a metal sieve to grade them for road making. Far left: A late nineteenth century roadmender poses with his tools, Hindringham, Norfolk.*

Right: *The introduction of steam road rollers in the latter decades of the nineteenth century enabled large-scale road making, with a consistent surface, possible for the first time since the Roman occupation of Britain. Improvements before then had been limited to particular highways and turnpikes. Now every lane could be made passable year-round. Here workers are making the road between Banff and MacDuff c.1910. Note the horses and carts used for transporting the roadstone.*

The Locomotive Act of 1861 enshrined in law the costs applicable to steam carriages using toll roads, relating them to the historic charges made for horse-drawn vehicles:

For every Locomotive propelled by any Power, containing within itself the Machinery for its own Propulsion, such a Toll for every Two Tons Weight or fractional part of every Two Tons Weight that such Locomotive shall weigh as shall be equal to the Toll or Tolls by their respective Acts made payable for every Horse drawing any Waggon, Wain, Cart, or Carriage with Wheels of a Width similar to those of such Locomotive...

On the farms it was the huge plough sets that first made a significant change from horse to steam power. These first appeared in the mid 1800s with various manufacturers vying to produce the best. Early innovators included John Heathcoat of Tiverton who attempted to build an engine running on canvas tracks in 1836, and before him a Mr Tindall who tried to produce a machine that emulated horses in that it 'walked' over the ground on legs. In 1879 farmer Thomas Darby, assisted by Robert Hasler, built a steam digger that moved forward on six 'feet', with protruding forks that turned over the ground at the rate of 1 acre an hour.

In truth none of these machines, whose actions required them to cross the ground they were working on, threatened existing horse-powered methods; they were simply too heavy. Heathcoat's engine, for instance, weighed in at 30 tons, and being left overnight in soft ground was simply swallowed up by the earth.

COUNTY COUNCIL OF DORSET. TAKE NOTICE THAT THIS BRIDGE (WHICH IS A COUNTY BRIDGE) IS INSUFFICIENT TO CARRY WEIGHTS BEYOND THE ORDINARY TRAFFIC OF THE DISTRICT; AND THAT THE OWNERS AND PERSONS IN CHARGE OF LOCOMOTIVE TRACTION ENGINES AND OTHER PONDEROUS CARRIAGES ARE WARNED AGAINST USING THE BRIDGE FOR THE PASSAGE OF ANY SUCH ENGINE OR CARRIAGE. E. ARCHDALL FFOOKS CLERK OF THE COUNTY COUNCIL OF DORSET

The development of the steam road roller was among the most significant factors in improving Britain's roads. For the first time it was possible, not only to carry sufficient roadstone or tarmacadam to where it was needed, but also to ensure that it was compacted to an extent where it withstood the wear of passing traffic and the effects of rain, ice and snow. Here, in 1895, a road gang work alongside a steam roller, with horses and carts providing roadstone and bitumen.

Thomas Darby's steam digger with Robert Hasler at the controls. Hasler had every reason to find alternative ways to working with horses. Aged nineteen, the son of a blacksmith, he had been kicked by a horse which resulted in an amputation of one of his legs.

Using a lighter engine farmer Richard Baker Harvey employes a fore-and-aft arrangement of triple-bladed ploughs that allow him to work backwards and forwards across a field in Calbourne on the Isle of Wight in 1912. Opposite: A steam plough set at work in Somerset c.1900.

The man credited with the successful development of the steam set and balance plough is John Fowler who, in 1858, was awarded a prize for his machine by the Royal Agricultural Society of England:

It is beyond question that Mr. Fowler's machine is able to turn over the soil and in an efficient manner at a saving compared with horse labour; while in all cases it is left in a far more desirable condition and better adapted for all the purposes of husbandry. We are unanimously of the opinion that he is fully entitled to the prize of £500.

Success came through the use of ploughing engines and counterbalanced ploughs, also known as balance ploughs, arranged so that as one plough did its work, the other (facing the opposite direction) was lifted clear of the ground. Fowler's machine worked via a single engine equipped with a windlass, sitting opposite an anchor carriage by which means the plough was drawn backwards and forwards across the field. Later, two engines were used, set at each extremity of a field and by means of a drum winch and cable they pulled the plough back and forth, inching forward as each set of furrows was completed. Such plough sets could, in experienced hands, plough 20 acres in a day, compared to 1 acre using horses.

But these massive machines, expensive to purchase and maintain, were suited to large and relatively flat farmland devoid of underlying rocks that could damage the plough. They were invariably owned by contractors who took the plough sets from farm to farm, employing a gang – usually four men and a boy – who travelled in a van towed by the steam engine, along with a water cart and other equipment. High boiler pressures and steel cables under extreme tension added to the dangers of working a plough set and accidents were not uncommon.

Driven by the increasing need to feed a growing population, as the nineteenth century drew to a close, the use of steam engines in farming had become commonplace, opening up land that had otherwise been difficult to cultivate and

Hauling, sawing, ploughing and threshing, tasks which were transformed by the arrival of the steam engine in farming.

Below: Steam traction for the first time gave the prospect of hauling loads far greater than was practicable using horses.

Opposite: A superb photograph, from Strumpshaw in Norfolk that captures the essence of threshing using a steam engine, with clouds of smoke mixing with the dust rising from the threshing drum. All that's missing is the infernal clatter of the machinery. The picture tells the complete story of the process: the horse has arrived from the rick with a full load of sheaves which are pitched to the man standing on top of the thresher. He shakes the sheaves loose into the top of the machine which separates the stalks, chaff and grain, disgorging each through separate chutes. Sacks full of grain are stacked in the foreground. Meanwhile the engine driver keeps the boiler going and regulates the speed of the thresher driven by the belt.

overcoming the increasing shortage of agricultural workers by reducing the numbers of men required for heavier tasks such as ploughing and threshing. Indeed it was in these areas, along with its capacity for hauling huge loads, that the traction engine had come into its own.

Threshing, or thrashing, that is removing the seeds of cereal grain from the inedible chaff and stalks, is one the most ancient tasks of the farming year. Traditionally this was done by beating the grain with flails, and allowing the wind to blow away the unwanted material. Early machine threshers, the first was invented by Andrew Meikle a Scottish engineer in the 1780s, were small and operated by horse power. Portable steam engines and traction engines from the mid nineteenth century onwards generated the sort of power that allowed threshing machines, also known as threshing drums, to be increased in size and capacity, speeding up what was considered among the most laborious of all farming jobs. Now, with the self-binder also in operation, the labour-intensive nature of the harvest and its aftermath was forever to change. Once gathered in:

...the sheaves would then be made into a rick in the farmyard, which was then thatched to keep the rain out until the great day came in the winter when the thrasher and trusser arrived. An appointment had to be made, the coal purchased and extra workers arranged to help. You would know when he was on his way when the man with the steam engine blew his whistle to warn you he was coming.

Sid Hunt worked for Father, driving the steam engine on threshing days. At about five he would stoke up the engine with coal and get up steam in time to give two blows on the whistle at six-thirty to warn the men he'd be setting off in half an hour. At five to seven he

"Threshing was a filthy job. For the two days of the thresh each stack would gradually be fed through the drum, the grain stripped from the straw and bagged at the end while other outlets spewed chaff and coulder (the husks). The emerging straw, stripped of its grain, was pitched and bunched to be stacked once more for use as animal litter throughout the coming year. The whole scene was engulfed in dust, smoke and steam, and from whatever direction the wind was coming it was always wrong for somebody. We would be up on the stack passing the sheaves down to the drum, where two men waited, one to cut the string round the sheaf and the other to feed the sheaves into the drum. Each had to be passed with ears of corn to the left. The old boy who looked after the 'chaff and coulder' was Billy Butt. His job was the dirtiest of the lot but he didn't mind. I don't think he ever washed because I never saw him clean."

96

Opposite page: *Steam threshing gang at Sticker in Cornwall early 1900s.*

Left: *Sawyers at work in the King's College timber yard at Sampford Courtenay in Devon c.1900. Baulks of timber would be drawn manually along rollers on the saw bed towards the circular saw driven by a belt from the traction engine.*

Below: *Around 1890 in the timber yard at Hemyock in Devon. The steam engine is of the portable type, being drawn by horse to wherever it was needed.*

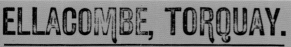

ELLACOMBE, TORQUAY.

To Contractors, Hauliers, Timber Merchants and Others.

Cessation for the time being of Contract to the Torquay Corporation Tramways.

RENDELL & SYMONS

Have been instructed by Mr. F. Drake (who has decided to dispose of his Horses, Carts, &c., owing to the reasons stated above), to

SELL BY AUCTION,

In a Field just beyond Bowmanville Terrace, Ellacombe,

On MONDAY, September 3rd, 1906,

At 2 p.m., the following grand lot of

CART HORSES

COBS, CARTS, TIMBER WAGONS, &c.

HORSES.

1—"BLOSSOM,' grey cart mare, 7 years old, 16-3 h.h., a grand mare, and admirably adapted for timber hauling or other heavy work.
2—"MADAM," roan cart mare, 7 years old, 16-2 h.h., would make an excellent match for No. 1.
3—"DARLING," black cart mare, 7 years old, 16-2 h.h.
4—"PRINCE," bay cart gelding, 8 years old, 16-1 h.h.
5—"CHARLIE," do. do.
6—"MADAM," bay cart mare, do. 16-2 h.h.
7—"VIOLET," brown cart mare, 7 years old, 17 h.h.
8—"LION," cart gelding, 8 years old, 16-2 h.h.
9—"BLACK PRINCE," black cart gelding, aged, 16-2 h.h.

10—"BOXER," dark brown cart gelding, aged, 16-3 h.h.
11—"BOB," brown cart gelding, aged, 15-2 h.h.
12—"FARMER," bay do. do. 17 h.h.
13—"PRINCE," bay gelding, 6 years old, 16 h.h., fit for 'bus, coaching, or Van work.
14—"POLLY," dun mare, 7 years old, 15 h.h., fit for Cab, 'Bus or Van work.
15—"DOLLY," bay mare, 10 years old, 16 h.h., fit for Cab, 'Bus, or Van work.
16—"BOB," a bay cob gelding, 8 years old, 14-1 h.h., a rare cob to go, and quiet to ride or drive.
17—"BILLY," a brown cob gelding, 7 years old, 13-0 h.h., a good worker, and quiet to ride or drive.
18—"LADY BIRD," a grey cob mare, aged, 15 h.h., wonderfully good little Mare, and a rare mover.

CARTS, HARNESS, &c., &c.

Undercarriage Timber Wagon, Top carriage do. to carry 10 tons, 10 Carts with sideboards, 2 Carts without do., Flat-bottom Wagon by "Jury" with Lades, 2 Spring Wagons to carry 15 cwt. and 13 cwt. respectively, nearly new Light Varnished Ralli Cart with Lamps and Cushions complete, nearly new Spring Trap with Cushions
12 Complete Sets of Cart Harness, all practically new ; 2 Sets of Fore Harness ; nearly new Set of Brown-plated Cob-size Trap Harness ; 4 full-size Sets of Black Trap Harness ; 12 Nosebags.

It is 1906 and the writing is literally on the wall for these horses, formerly used under contract to the Torbay Corporation Tramway and now redundant. Thousands of other animals at this time were coming back on to the market due to a number of factors including the electrification of tramways and the introduction of mechanically powered road vehicles.

gave a single blow and finally, at seven, a long whistle gave the signal for work. Then he pulled a lever and the big driving wheel started slowly to pull on the long belt and, blowing out steam in all directions, thrashing would start with every man in the correct place doing his own particular job.

It was a job fraught with dangers and the author recalls in his boyhood in Cornwall standing atop the tractor-driven thresher using a pitchfork to push the sheaves into the clattering maw of the machinery, a dark hole in which levers and cranks literally thrashed around. It took only a moment's distraction to see the pitchfork tugged from my grasp and disappear into the machine – to emerge after a few additional bangs from the nether end of the machine, now in several pieces.

In the nineteenth century local papers were full of reports of accidents caused while threshing; this from the *Bury & Norwich Post*:

There has not been any recent inventions by which human calamity has been produced as by the new implement called the thrashing machine and this in greater measure arises from unskilfulness of those employed to work it and are often ignorant of the powers of mechanism. We notice that Mr Arthur Brooks of Horringer had a very narrow escape within the last few days as the whole of his cloathes, even his shirt was torn from his back and had not his men stopped the machine with such promptitude there would have been loss of limbs and probably his life. It would therefore be prudent to prohibit the use of the implement under penalty unless attended by a skillful mechanic.

Threshing drums continued to be used well into the 1960s and beyond, now driven from the power take-off from tractors. Today, along with steam powered ploughing sets and sawmills, they feature in various steam fairs held around the country, attracting huge followings.

But steam was never to fully usurp the place of the horse on the farm. The engines were too heavy and cumbersome to use on much of Britain's farmland, and the cost prohibitive. But, at the turn of the century, a new threat to horsepower was about to emerge in the form of petrol and oil-burning engines. In 1902 Dan Albone produced the first commercially successful tractor, the three-wheel Ivel, which directly challenged the horse with regard to the work it was designed to do. And within a little over a decade later, much worse was to come for the horse at the outbreak of the First World War.

The Great War

In my book *The War Horses* I argue that the First World War formed the watershed from which it is possible to discern the point at which the eventual disappearance of the horse from the British landscape became inevitable. A bond which had lasted for thousands of years between man and horse was broken in those four years of war and all its trappings swept away almost entirely within the next three decades.

We have already seen that the drive for greater efficiency in agriculture, in order to produce more food, was leading inexorably towards mechanical power and away from the horse, and that the rural population was migrating to cities whose growth was fuelled by industrialisation. On the eve of the Industrial Revolution in the 1750s only around 10 per cent of Britain's people lived in cities, by the end of the nineteenth century almost 90 per cent did so, during which time the population had grown from 7 to 37 million. For the horse this also meant a move into the towns and cities where their numbers, working in haulage and transport, rose from 230 000 in 1870 to around 490 000 at the outbreak of war in 1914.

At the outbreak of the war, many of Britain's major towns and cities had moved away from horse transport towards electric tramways. In London for instance the first electric tram appeared in 1901, and by 1915 the last horse tram had been withdrawn.

Above: *The opening of the electric tram service in Carshalton, Surrey, October 1906. These vehicles replaced horse-drawn buses and horse trams.*

Left: *Horses and carts weave around Bournemouth-based trams in the High Street, Poole, Dorset in 1913.*

GOODBYE OLD FRIEND

The advent of the electric tram and the continued expansion of the railway into the most remote parts of the country, the introduction of steam traction engines, early combustion-engined vehicles, and the bicycle, ran hand in hand with improvements and expansion of the country's road network, each eroding the dominance of horse power.

The direct effect of the First World War on the later rapid decline of horse power in Britain was the result of three principal events:

1. Millions of men, many leaving farming to join the army, hundreds of thousands of whom are killed.

2. Hundreds of thousands of horses taken to war of which many are killed.

3. The rapid development of technology (new weapons and means of transport were developed in months that otherwise would have taken years) and the consequent rise in the number of mechanical vehicles and trained drivers at the war's end, and the import and manufacture of large numbers of tractors to alleviate food shortages.

In August 1914 Kitchener made a special appeal to agricultural workers to join the army once the harvest was over. Here local men stand in civilian clothes alongside militiamen at Williton station in Somerset having 'taken the King's shilling'.

Here we will look in more detail at these factors and how they together accelerated the decline of the horse. We will also look at some of the indirect influences that the war had upon our relationship with the horse; more subtle effects which contributed to the breaking of those bonds. We are concerned here principally with the working horse at war, and not the animals used by the cavalry and various artillery units.

Crowds of wellwishers gather to wave off soldiers and recruits at Axminster station in Devon, August 1914.

*   *   *

The British Army at the outbreak of the war in 1914 comprised 733 000 men, and by 1918 the total allied forces could command 8.5 million, almost 5.5 million serving on the Western Front. In the first month of the conflict Lord Kitchener recruited a further 750 000 volunteers, doubling the number of his forces. In popular imagination these volunteers were eager to 'get at the Boche', fighting for King and Country, but while many were caught up in the fervour of patriotism, many young men were simply pleased to find a way out of the hardship of working on the land. Decades of unrest, low pay and poor housing had already driven thousands to look overseas for

Contemporary postcard making light of the recruitment process.

a better life, while at home 25 per cent of the population was said to be living in poverty. Even in the years running up to the war, farmworkers were looking to escape from the land, as George Ewart Evans' interviewees in *Akenfield* recall:

It must seem there was a war between farmers and their men in those days. These employers were famous for their meanness. They took all they could from the men and boys who worked the land. They bought their life's strength for as little as they could. Fourteen young men left the village in 1909-11 to join the army. There wasn't a recruiting drive, they just escaped.

Another young man put it even more succinctly:

When the farmer stopped my pay because it was raining and we couldn't thrash, I said to my seventeen-year-old mate. 'Bugger him, we'll go and join the army.'

And a third, having been recruited, found life was transformed, albeit temporarily for the better:

In my four months' training with the regiment I put on nearly a stone in weight. They said it was the food but it was really because for the first time in my life there had been

Those used to working with horses were eagerly recruited into mounted units or to serve with the Army Service Corps which was directly responsible for transport and supply in the British army. Here Royal North Devon Hussars wait to depart from Barnstaple railway station in 1914, with a large crowd in the background coming to wave them off. The photograph gives some idea of the logistical problems that the transport of so many men, their horses and equipment would pose. It is an irony that this mounted regiment's first posting would be to the East Coast of England and thereafter, without their horses, they were shipped to the Dardanelles.

no strenuous work... We were all delighted when war broke out on August 4th. I was now a machine gunner in the Third Essex Regiment. A lot of boys from the village were with me and though we were all sleeping in ditches at Harwich, wrapped in our great-coats, we were bursting with happiness. We were all damned glad to have got off the farms.

These recollections paint rather a different picture of the popular view of young men eager for the fight. They also remind us that farmwork, the men often working along-side horses, was for both man and beast, often a life of unremitting drudgery.

Once at the front, of course, these soldiers would quickly have realised they were simply replacing one kind of hell for another. Almost a million British soldiers died and many of them took with them the intimate details of working the land and dealing daily with horses; skills and secrets that had been passed down from father to son, from one generation to the next over centuries. Things that could never be learned from books, now lost in the mud of a foreign field.

Above and below: *Casualties on the battle-field; the reality of war for both men and horses.*

The great and the good were keen to 'do their bit' for the war effort. The author John Galsworthy was among those who 'volunteered' his favourite horse Peggy for active service in 1914. But, much to his relief, his offer was turned down.

The recruitment of horses was no less urgent than that for men. The Army had long recognised that future conflicts would require increasing numbers of horses. To this end they had various of strategies in hand to ensure an adequate supply in the event of war. These included, at the end of the nineteenth century, the establishment of the Army Remounts Department which was specifically tasked with selecting and training horses for the military. And in 1887 the government introduced a scheme which allowed owners of horses to register their animals for use by the army in return for a subsidy towards the cost of upkeep, and a guaranteed purchase price in the event of the registered animals being called up in time of war. There was also of course the option of purchasing horses on the open market. In August 1914 the army had 25 000 animals in hand for transport duties and required, immediately, five times that number. At this time they had an inventory of only 80 motor vehicles and horses were the only means by which the mobility of the armed forces could be guaranteed.

One option open to the government was to make a general call for horses to be 'volunteered' for service. But this 'loaning' of horses proved insufficient, and the government were obliged to implement a system of impressment under the Army Act. This involved setting up groups of commissioners who were charged with the task of requiring horse owners in given districts to bring forward their animals for selection. With the help of retired army officers, accompanied by serving soldiers' over 165 000 horses had been 'requisitioned' within a few weeks.

'Traveller', a handsome Shire horse at Brunsell's Farm near Staunton Caundle in Dorset was sold to the Army Remounts Department (who were responsible for finding and training horses for the army) by farmer Alban Harris in November 1914. That a photograph should be taken of the event is some indication of the significance given to support for the war effort in the early months of the war. Even so, not all farmers were happy to see their horses go, as one farmworker recalls: 'A lot of farmers hid their horses during the Great War, when the officers came around. The officers always gave them good money for a horse but sometimes the horses were like brothers and the men couldn't let them go, so they hid them.'

O.H.M.S.

IMPRESSMENT OF HORSES

Notification is hereby given that under Section 115 of the Army Act—

MAJOR H. E. J. EYRE,
Horwood House, Bideford,
N. Devon

has been authorised by the Army Council to impress by purchase in North Devon such animals as may be required for the use of His Majesty's Forces.

Above: Notices like this appeared up and down the country. Armed with lists of the numbers of horses owned, and by whom, in each district, the commissioners had various criteria from which their selection was made; light and heavy draught, pack horses etc.

Above left: It is late 1914 and here we see a troop of farm horses being ridden into Kingsbridge, Devon, for selection by the army. It is noticeable that the farmhands riding them are using sacks for saddles and only basic bridles which suggests that they are expecting these mounts to be taken for the war effort.

Left: This is the scene in Hatherleigh, North Devon, in August 1914. Horseman and farmhands stand with their charges waiting for the army commissioners to make their selection.

Beaminster, Dorset in 1914 where a large crowd has gathered to watch the commissioners select horses for the war.

The story of these horses, the work they were called upon to perform, and the suffering they underwent is told in full in my book *The War Horses*. It is enough here simply to state the bare facts. It is estimated that the total number of horses mules and donkeys killed on all sides and in all theatres of war between 1914 and 1918 was 8 million – a million fewer than the total estimated human military casualties – while 2.5 million horses had been treated in veterinary hospitals, of which 2 million had been restored successfully enough for the animal to return to duty. During the course of the war the British Army on the Western Front had 256 000 horses killed (558 000 British soldiers died in same theatre).

It might naturally be surmised from these figures that the immense slaughter of these animals in just four years had a lasting and direct effect in the immediate aftermath of the war in relation to the numbers of horses then available. But this was not the case, and the death of so many animals was the least significant factor of the three under consideration here in relation to the eventual decline of horse power; the death of men being of far greater significance. Indeed, in the years following the war the numbers of working horses available for agricultural and other purposes actually rose slightly. In 1910 there had been 1.18 million and in 1920 1.20 million working horses in Britain.

*"Heaving about in the filthy mud of
the road was an unfortunate mule
with both of his forelegs shot away.
The poor brute, suffering God knows
what untold agonies and terrors, was
trying desperately to get to its feet
which weren't there. Writhing and
heaving, tossing its head about in its
wild attempts, not knowing that it
no longer had any front legs."*

Lt R.G. Dixon, Royal Garrison Artillery

Above: *French soldiers attempt to rescue a mule which has fallen into a water-filled
shell hole and lies exhausted. A second animal has already been pulled from the mud
and stands on the left.* Below: *Mutilated carcases of horses lie on the battlefield at
Passchendaele, 1917.*

As with Kitchener's famous 'Your County Needs You Poster' which rallied hundreds of thousands to volunteer in the first months of the war, so it was a poster that helped galvanise the animal welfare groups. Fortunino Matania, a young Italian artist, produced a painting which served as an icon for those raising monies for the care of animals in the war. The painting, 'Goodbye Old Man' remains a powerful image and is of course the inspiration behind the title of this book.

This seeming anomaly is explained by the fact that, as the war progressed, the authorities had begun to fill the gap between the number of animals required and those available, principally through purchasing horses from overseas. Improving veterinary care also mitigated the earlier shortages. The British Army Veterinary Corps hospitals treated 725,000 horses in France over the course of the war, successfully healing around 520 000. Of the 2.5 million animals treated by the AVC, 80 per cent were returned to duty.

At home too, farmers had recovered from the loss of animals through impressment, replacing lost animals through breeding and, again, through the purchase of imports. And more significant than all these factors was that, as the war ended, thousands of now redundant animals were put on to the market by the military. By 1919 almost a quarter of a million horses were sold at home and abroad, raising almost £8 million, a small recovery when set against the total cost to Britain in purchasing horses throughout the duration of the war of £67.5 million.

That horses were returned to Britain at all was to no small extent due to the pressure put on the military authorities by animal welfare charities such as the RSPCA and the Blue Cross whose work throughout the war had done much to improve the lot of the horse. Now they lobbied Parliament to stop the indiscriminate sale of horses in France and Belgium, insisting that they be returned to a life in farming rather than ending their days on the butcher's block. Around 45 000 animals it is estimated were sold on the Continent.

'Please Help Our Wounded Comrades at the Front'. A Devon beach donkey is called upon to play its part in raising money for the RSPCA's Fund for Sick and Wounded Horses c.1916.

In February 1919, Winston Churchill, Secretary of State for War, took a personal interest in the plight of these animals. The Ministry of Shipping had promised a return of 12 000 horses a week but failed to achieve even a quarter of that number. Churchill demanded answers from Lt-General Sir Travers Clarke, Quartermaster General:

If it is so serious, what have you been doing about it? The letter of the Commander-In-Chief discloses a complete failure on the part of the Ministry of Shipping to meet its obligations and scores of thousands of horses will be left in France under extremely disadvantageous conditions.

As a consequence, the number of animals transported back to Britain rose to around 9000 per week, but the reality was that the government, the public and the military had more pressing things on their minds. Europe was in the grip of the Spanish Flu epidemic that killed at least three times the number who had died in the war. Many families were near starvation and there was pressure to reduce the country's reliance on expensive imported food and to get British farming back on its feet. In February 1919 a Board of Agriculture and Fisheries report complained that the Department of Demobilisation and Resettlement had been dilatory in getting men back to work on the land. Those skilled in ploughing etc. had been designated as 'pivotal' men and 29 792 of these had been given priority release.

Fortunino Matania's original painting.

"OLD TOMMY"

1914.

1924.

1934.

A number of cavalry officers, who took their own mounts to war, brought them back safely. A postcard given to the author by a relative of Lt-Col. J. Scott Bowden who had taken 'Old Tommy' to war and returned with him in 1919. On the back of the card is printed the following details: 'Foal Dumfriesshire 1906. Purchase Carlisle 1911. Trained annually with the Westd. and Cumbd. Yeomanry until 1914. Mobilized Penrith, with the Westd. and Cumbd. Yeomanry, August 5th 1914. Embarked with HQ 53rd (Welsh) Div. T.A. for Egypt, 1915. Served with 53rd (Welsh) Div. T.A., M.E.F. until demobilization at Alexandria, 1919. Returned via Southampton to Whitehaven, 1919. Still going strong and doing his bit, 1935.' A handwritten note is appended, 'died 1940'.

Early in the war British forces were obliged to call upon any available sources for transporting troops and equipment. This is a former Putney bus converted for use as pigeon loft on the Western Front.

The war brought about a great many innovations in weaponry and machines. This Holt 75 tractor pointed the way to the development of future industrial and agricultural machinery, not least the bulldozer which the Caterpillar Company of America later developed from this machine. Over 1300 of these tractors were supplied for use by the British forces and they took over from horses the task of hauling increasing large guns and supply trains and in retrieving stranded vehicles from the battlefield.
Photo courtesy Paul Rackham.

It is estimated that as few as 60 000 animals eventually returned to Britain, and the truth is that while the repatriation of these horses met the sensitivities of the British public, there was, once initial demand for work horses had been satisfied, little call for animals that had suffered the rigours of war, many showing signs of temperamental damage, others exhibiting characteristics of army training which made them unsuitable for civilian use, as Londoner 'Nick' Nichols recalled to the author:

My uncle bought a horse from the army after the war. I remember it had letters branded into its hoofs. He fancied himself a bit of an circus acrobat and would trot around standing up on the back of the horse. One day my brother got hold of a bugle and blew it; you should have seen this horse take off with my uncle on its back. Whoosh!

Painful as it is to consider that many of these animals who 'had done their bit' were by 1919 simply 'surplus to requirements', their redundancy was in part assured by the miraculous advances in technological developments over four short years. While much of this activity was concentrated upon weapon development, tanks, poison gas and military aircraft being chief among these, the major concern for the armies on all sides was to reduce their reliance upon horse power, not least, for the British Army, in order to reduce the 5000 tons of fodder per day required to feed them.

The so-called White Heat of technological development that was driven by war gave rise to weapons and machines that had never been seen on the battlefield. The rapidity of this progress greatly accelerated the decline of horse power. Above: British bombers on an airfield in France, 1917. Above right: Despatch rider Corporal Bromley Penny on his motorcycle. Below left: British light tanks on the Western Front c.1916. Below right: A troop of heavy tanks in 1917.

Above: *In the months following the war's end the military forces looked to shed themselves of thousands of vehicles now surplus to requirements. Many of Britain's haulage companies began with vehicles purchased at relatively low prices in this period. During the First World War the Huddersfield-based Karrier' company had provided the military with 2000 chassis on which a variety of bodies were built. This vehicle, photographed at Hethersett in Norfolk around 1920, has all the look of an army surplus machine. Note the solid tyres.*

Above right: *Steam lorries and motor lorries lined up at a Royal Navy base at the end of the war. Such machines, many of them at the sharp end of technological development, came on to the market in large numbers in 1919.*

At the war's outset the army owned fewer than 100 motorised vehicles, by November 1918 this had risen to 57 000 lorries and tractors, 23 000 light road vehicles and 7000 motor ambulances. Large numbers of these now became available on the open market. Added to this was the government's 1917 plan to import and produce more tractors in order to increase food production and this resulted in a sudden bonanza of mechanical transport. Moreover, while the 'ploughmen of England' who had signed up in their millions (and died in their thousands) could not be replaced, soldier-engineers, familiar with petrol and diesel engines formed an eager workforce willing to take over.

*   *   *

Clouds of change that for some years before the Great War had begun to accumulate and cast their shade over the future of horse power, threw their darkest shadow in the years between 1914-18. The slaughter of men and animals alike hastened the end of the working horse in Britain, as did advances in technology, but as we shall examine in the next chapter, it was social and political changes after the war that also finally compounded the horse's fate.

Goodbye Old Friend

There is the village in my mind's eye, as it was... the age-long routine of Cornish life still unbroken, though perhaps like an old grandfather clock it was winding down slowly, imperceptibly, to a stop. The War – till lately 'the War' still meant in these parts the Great War of 1914–18: evidence perhaps of the slowness of adaptation, the tenacity of our minds – the War brought all that life of habit to a sudden full stop, held it suspended, breathless for a full four years in the shadow of its wing, and meanwhile set in being motions and tendencies which came to full flood the moment the War was over and swept away the old landmarks in a tide of change... In the pre-war years of which I am writing, the continuity of custom was still unbroken... The old social structure has at length been broken, like a pitcher at the well, the pieces dispersed. And the same with many of the old customs and ways.

Cornwall as A.L. Rowse would have known it before the First World War. The miller's cart stands outside the mill at St Keyne, early 1900s.

These are the words of Cornish man of letters, A.L. Rowse, from *A Cornish Childhood*, published in 1942. He echoes the sentiments of many who had lived through the Great War; the world they had known was gone forever.

N.S. LANDER & SON.
ST KEYNE
ROLLER FLOUR MILLS

With the chance of employment poor for able-bodied men returning from the war, for the 1.6 million British wounded the prospects were even more bleak. Hospitals treated over 80 000 cases of shell shock and for these victims many were never to return to civilian life. Others had to rely on charity or on menial jobs such as match-selling on the streets. Even the uninjured faced disillusionment:

...when at last we came home, were demobilised and doffed our uniforms, we realised how much our welcome had depended on the glamour of our clothes, with all that they implied. In mufti we were no longer heroes, we were simply 'unemployed', an unpleasant problem.

A government poster from 1917 reminds a hungry British population of the stark choice between guns and bread. In 1918 came rationing under the Defence of the Realm Act.

The world was different too for the men who came back from the war, or at least many were determined not to return to the life they had left. Not only had they been told by Prime Minister Lloyd George that they would return 'to a fit land for heroes to live in', they carried with them a determination that the hardships they had suffered would not be futile. George Ewart Evans records the zeal of one such returning soldier, Len Thompson:

Len is also an extraordinarily interesting survivor of Britain's village lost generation, that mysterious army of horsemen, ploughmen and fieldworkers who fled the wretchedness of the farms in 1914. The army had provided and escape route for many years before this, but it was the First World War which swept Len and his contemporaries off the land to conditions which forced the thinking countrymen to decide to halt a system of degradation when they returned. The climate of the 1920s and 1930s suited Len perfectly for what he had to do. The war had given those who survived it confidence. Len showed his by solidly denying the village farmers their virtual ownership of the labourers and their families. He organised a union branch.

War had opened the eyes of many to the iniquities of their former state as labourers, whether in the fields or factories. The revolution in Russia and similar unrest in Europe fomented strong feeling against the established order among British workers, a movement that was supported by growing numbers of politicians and intellectuals.

Campaigning author Arthur Mee, in his pamphlet 'Who Giveth Us the Victory', an analysis of the outcome of the First World War, describes the world as it will be for the soldiers who return from the fighting:

It is pitiful to think that thousands of these men have better homes in the trenches of Flanders than in the sunless alleys of our motherland. Do thousands of children come into the world to gasp for life in a slum, to go to school hungry for a year or two, to pick up a little food, a little slang, or a little arithmetic, to grovel in the earth for forty years or to stand in the steaming factories, to wear their bodies out like cattle on the land, to live in little rows of dirty houses, or little blocks of stuffy rooms, and then to die?

Those who imagined they would return to a land of promise, where jobs would be waiting for them, were met instead by food shortages and rising unemployment. In January 1918, sugar was rationed and by the end of April meat, butter, cheese and margarine were added to the list of rationed food. Ration cards were issued and everyone had to register with a butcher and grocer.

Added to the men's discontent was the presence of woman workers who had taken over many of the occupations formerly held by them. From 1915, in order to meet the acute food shortage, the Board of Agriculture organised the Women's Land Army

'Sold Out - No more goods expected today.' Long after the war's end, food shortages remained acute and rationing of foodstuffs continued for months. Meat remained on ration until December 1919, butter until May 1920 and sugar until November of that year.

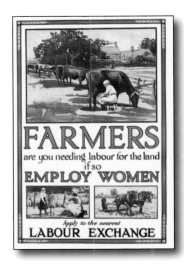

Steam remained a prime source of motive power well into the twentieth century. Here is a steam roller at work in Buckfastleigh, Devon. It is interesting to note in this photograph, taken a year after the war, that the men are dressed in a combination of old army uniform and civilian dress.

Women on war work at the Westland air-craft factory in Somerset c.1916. Note they are wearing the badges denoting their official status.

Above right: A young woman on horseback dressed in Women's Land Army Uniform at Teigngrace in Devon c.1917.

Right: A photograph by Olive Edis, one of the few women official photographers in France. Here she has captured FANY drivers in Calais: 'A very jolly type of good class English girl they were – some of a decidedly sporting and masculine stamp.'

which, by the end of 1917, saw around 250 000 women working as farm labourers of whom 20 000 were WLA members. Thousands of other women worked in factories.

Some women had volunteered as drivers earlier in the war, usually ladies of the wealthier 'county set' who had their own cars and who acted as unofficial chauffeurs for those on vital war work.

The First Aid Nursing Yeomany, formed in 1907, ran field hospitals, drove ambulances and organised troop canteens and soup kitchens. Many of these women ended the war with greater experience of motor vehicles than the fighting men.

This was the first time the nation had faced Total War in which the civilian population was engaged alongside its armed forces. In farming, despite the initial resentment of farmers, the appearance of women whose role had traditionally been limited largely to dairy work, now undermined the centuries-old male-dominated world of the horseman. And though much of the campaigning by the suffrage movement had been suspended during the years of conflict, in 1918 under the Representation of the People Act over 8 million women gained the vote for the first time.

In all these things, as the old social orders were swept aside by war, so the ties between the horse, men and the land continued to dissolve.

*   *   *

Consumed by the growing crises of food supplies, in 1917 the government took over 2.5 million acres of otherwise largely unproductive land in order to open it up to food production. The horses required to plough this new acreage were in short supply as was, despite the thousands of women now employed, the skilled manpower. Much as they had done earlier to solve the shortage of horses, the authorities now looked to North America for aid in providing tractors and ploughs. In March 1917, a report by the Government Food Production Department records:

> *It has been ascertained that there is a total of 459 tractors of various makes on order of which 35 are expected to Dock at Liverpool on the 4th inst. The actual number of tractors already bought and already in use is 32.*

A month later the situation is not much improved, as a report to the War Cabinet in April 1917 makes clear:

> *The provision of tractors and ploughs is a much more anxious matter. Owing to shipping and other difficulties the importation of American machinery has been exceedingly disappointing. Of the 600 tractors and 214 ploughs ordered only 78 tractors and 108 ploughs have been delivered.*

Top: *Women gathering flax near Ilchester 1917.* Centre: *Scything weeds at Lamerton, Devon c.1918.* Bottom: *Miss Collet under instruction, ploughing at Foxworthy, Devon.*

An original Ford Model F manufactured by Henry Ford & Son in Dearborn, Michigan in 1917. It is powered by a 4-cylinder petrol-paraffin engine generating 20hp. This particular machine was purchased by the Ministry of Munitions and arrived in Britain early in 1918 and did not bear the familiar Fordson radiator badge of later versions. It took a farmer an hour and a half to till an acre of ground with five horses and a gang plow. With a tractor like this and a moldboard plow, it took only a half-hour to plow an acre.
Photo courtesy Paul Rackham.

The 'Universal G' was made in 1916 by British engineer Hebert Saunderson who produced more tractors during the First World War than any other British company.
Photo courtesy Paul Rackham.

The same Cabinet report suggests that production of American tractors under licence in Britain would be one way to solve this difficulty: an idea that arises from a not entirely selfless suggestion by British industry:

The only solution, so far as the bulk of supply is concerned, appears, therefore, to be to develop the suggestions made by a group of British motor manufacturers that they should combine resources to produce a replica of the Ford tractor, which is extremely simple, and cheap, and has proved its practical value after a severe and extended trial.

Eventually an order for 5000 tractors (later increased to 6000) was placed with Ford in America and within five months the order had been fulfilled, with the machines being shipped to the Ford Motor Company Ltd in Britain for final assembly. These were Fordson Model F tractors which, in the US had been made available for the equivalent of under £200. Almost overnight people in the countryside began to see tractors displacing teams of horses. While British-made tractors had been available from the early years of the century there is little doubt that this sudden influx of mass-produced machines, simple to maintain and operate, with spares easily obtainable, gave perceptible impetus to the age of the small tractor.

GOODBYE OLD FRIEND

By the mid 1920s Ford had captured around 75 per cent of the market for tractors in Britain and these created the blueprint for cost and reliability by which other manufacturers set their standards. Companies at home and overseas such as Case, Ferguson, International, Allis Chalmers, John Deere, Farmall, McCormick and many others great and small grew, amalgamated or faded into obscurity over the next two decades. While many early machines were simple enough mechanically to survive the repair and maintenance by the local blacksmith, the bigger companies began to establish their own dealerships, with engineering shops equipped to service the needs of local farmers. Agricultural activity was thus being removed from the purely local economy and the livelihoods of those who had previous serviced it, the saddlers, harnessmakers, farriers and the like, found themselves swept out of business by the rising tide of change.

Above: *International Harvester grew out of the merger of various smaller companies in the USA. In 1918 it introduced the IH 8-16 Junior which continued in production until 1922. Around 2500 were imported into Britain.* Photo courtesy Paul Rackham.

Below: *An IH 8-16 Junior at work towing a reaper-binder , Blofield, Norfolk, in 1920.*

"Looking back I can see that the arrival of the village bus was one of the first nails in the saddler's coffin. One farmer had a motor-plough, it is true, but he was rich. The bus told me motors wouldn't always be for the rich."

Harry Rose - Saddler

Mowing at New Barn Farm Calbourne in 1922 using a Fordson Model F towing a Bamford mower. The stick was used to clear grass from the clogged blades!

THE AUSTIN
FARM TRACTOR

THE AUSTIN FARM TRACTOR
MAKES LAND VALUABLE

Herbert Austin was a member of a committee set up during the First World War by the government to look at producing tractors in the UK. Henry Ford, who had been the main source of supply, agreed to allow his machines to be assembled in Britain for use by the Ministry of Munitions and Austin began to look into manufacturing his own tractor, the first of which came off the production line in 1919.

Horses gave way to tractor power at Westover Park Farm in 1928. Here Ted Harvey is driving an Overtime model imported from the USA by Harry Ferguson, an Irish engineer who was to have a huge impact on the later development of agricultural machinery.

"During the early part of the Great War some American tractors arrived – huge big things, nearly as vast as traction engines. We didn't worry too much because they couldn't be used in wet weather."

Above: *The 'Titan' produced by the International Harvester Company from 1915. Running on kerosene it was to a large extent an internal combustion replacement for steam engines, especially for belt driven work.*
Photo courtesy Paul Rackham.

Above left: *A Titan 10-20 pulling a mower at Birchanger Farm, Porlock, 1930s.*

Left: *The rapid development of the internal combustion engine heralded in the age of cheap motoring, at least for the upper middle classes. Taking the lead of Henry Ford in utilising the production line process, Herbert Austin embarked upon a small car made for the masses, the Austin 7. First sold in 1922 and costing around £175, Austin finally ceased production of the model in 1939 and by that time had sold 290 000 vehicles. Austin also made tractors. Companies that once had sold carriages, now became garages selling and repairing vehicles of all types. This is Batten Bros. garage in Cullompton, Devon in the late 1920s. Note the Fordson tractor sign above the entrance.*

GOODBYE OLD FRIEND

This graph shows how the decline in the use of horses in agriculture mirrors the rise in the number of tractors, with the agricultural workforce declining steadily from 1920 onwards, with variations decade by decade. The principal period of growth in mechanised farming was between 1930 and 1960 when the numbers of tractors increased 33-fold from about 12 000 to over 400 000, by which time Britain had the highest density of tractors and the highest number of tractors per head of population in the world. Over the same period the number of horses fell by a factor of 8 to fewer than 100 000 by 1960 and thereafter became something of a curiosity where they remained at all on farms.
Graph based on 'Trends in Mechanisation', Ministry of Agriculture, 1984.

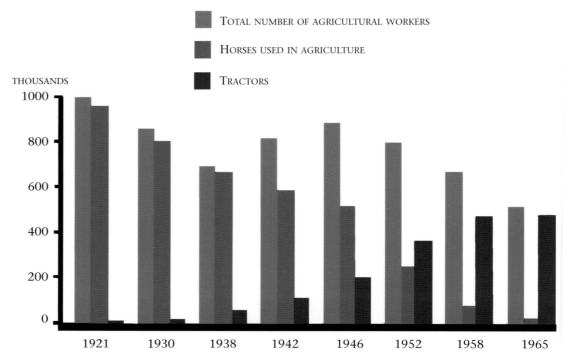

TOTAL NUMBER OF AGRICULTURAL WORKERS

HORSES USED IN AGRICULTURE

TRACTORS

THOUSANDS

1000 · 800 · 600 · 400 · 200 · 0

1921   1930   1938   1942   1946   1952   1958   1965

Art meets industrial design - a car bonnet mascot by Lalique from 1925. Some irony that the horse should be chosen to represent elegance, speed and potency on the front of a vehicle that usurped its position as the transport means of choice for the wealthy elite.

And yet, amid the despondency felt by returning soldiers and the poor economic climate of the immediate post-war years, there was a growing movement towards reaching for a brighter future. Born of a determination among many to make a better world for themselves, despite the gloom, the mood of the times was taken up by artists and musicians – the 'Roaring Twenties' had arrived.

Known in France as the 'années folles' (the crazy years), this perhaps more accurately describes a society dislocated from the political realities but fuelled by a heady mix of a desire to forget the past and embrace the novelty brought about by innovation: the phonograph, the telephone, motion pictures, electric light and not least the automobile. Short-lived though it was, the period saw strides forward in industrial design (allied to the art deco movement that began in Paris in 1920), in which form was believed to be as important as function. Nowhere was this more apparent than in the machines associated with travel: aircraft, boats and in particular the automobile. (Agricultural vehicles would generally lack much other than functionality in their design). In pre-war Italy Futurism glorified the concepts of the future, embracing speed and technology, and it was the spirit of these movements that later inspired young

'The Charge of the Lancers', by Italian Futurist Umberto Boccioni was painted in 1915, shortly before the artist, then serving in an artillery regiment, was thrown from his horse and killed. The zeal of the followers of Futurism was ended by the disillusionment, of war, but their spirit lived on in many of the post-war cultural attitudes.

men in Britain to embrace all the excitements of the modern age. Against this background the horse was as culturally redundant as the stovepipe hat.

Few could afford cars in the 1920s and 30s, but many of those who might formerly have worked on the land now took the opportunity to escape to the cities to work in car and aircraft plants. Others, who in earlier times may have become apprenticed to the local blacksmith, now chose the local garage where they could at least take a car out for testing from time to time if not actually own one.

Even as the decline of the horse in agriculture was accelerating to its eventual doom, it remained a potent symbol of power, especially in the design of cars. This bonnet mascot was designed by Casimir Brau in 1925. Around this time Enzo Ferrari chose the prancing horse symbol for his own cars.

The need for speed. A hill climb event at Porlock in Somerset shortly before the First World War. This sort of event grew more popular in post-war years with access to cheap second-hand cars. Note the motorcycle in the background.

123

And those interested in speed, but with limited means, turned to motorcycles which exemplified to these young men the freedom of the open road.

This growth in mechanised transport and the public's view that ownership of a vehicle conferred status, as the horse once had done, pushed the horse further back into history. By the mid 1930s there were around 2.5 millions cars on the road in Britain, a number that had grown from 15 000 only twenty years earlier.

Wardill's cycle shop and garage before the outbreak of war. Already cars were beginning to be seen as the future of public transport, with motorcycles providing the same individual freedom of travel, but at an affordable price.

Steam-powered vehicles remained on the scene well into the 1940s, though like the horse, their days were numbered. Traction engines survived on farms, principally to provide stationary power for belt-driven machinery such as threshing drums, and steam road rollers continued in service until these were replaced by diesel-engined models. On small farms, steam engines were used for as long as they were serviceable, with farmers, as ever, reluctant to replace machinery due to cost unless absolutely necessary. Others in farming faced problems of a more unusual nature:

We had steam engines on the farm before I was born. We bought a new one in 1921. I can remember it coming home. But we didn't use it for four years because the old man who used to drive our engines was a dirty old B— and father said when he retires we'll use it. That cost us a thousand pounds.

The slump of the early 1930s had hit agriculture particularly badly, further hardening farmers against change. In 1931 the NFU president announced:

It is impossible to exaggerate the seriousness of the situation. I fail to see what is going to happen to the British farmer unless some drastic remedial steps are taken. I don't very much mind what line is adopted so long as the British farmer is given a fair chance to meet the cost of production and to live. The corn harvest is upon us and yet our products are practically valueless. I can see nothing but bankruptcy for hundreds of farmers.

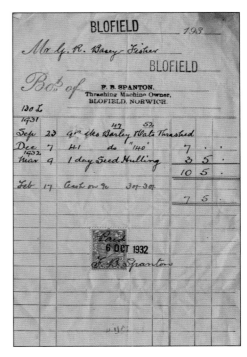

A 1932 bill for threshing barley and seed hulling from F.B. Spanton, Blofield, Norfolk.

Still under steam well into the 1920s and 30s, a traction engine and threshing drum at St Ervan in Cornwall.

GOODBYE OLD FRIEND

The size and immense weight of steam engines, coupled to the weight and quantity of coal and water required to fuel them, put them at a disadvantage against the increasing number of internal-combustion engined vehicles appearing in the early years of the twentieth century. The massive plough sets continued in use into the 1940s, as did steam road rollers, as weight was a positive advantage for these applications.

Right: But sometimes weight brought difficulties in control. A Fowler traction engine comes to grief in the late 1920s.

A steam engine auction in Norfolk in 1930. To some extent the coming on to the market of cheap machines such as these undermined the rise in tractor sales for companies such as Ford who continually looked to reduce the price of their tractors to see off competition.

The end of steam. A stationary engine rusting away in a quarry on Portland in 2005.

A convoy of steam traction engines line up at Cullompton railway station about to make their last journey to the scrapyard in 1952.

Echoes of an earlier era in farming resonated well into the mid twentieth century. Apart from a dogged resistance to change, old ways died hard in the countryside where a traditional way of life was held in high regard. Farmers were reluctant to discard equipment that had become familiar and continued to provide good service, and the cost of new machinery was a further barrier to modernisation. Here, in the late 1930s, threshing continues much as it had in the 1890s with steam engine, threshing drum and a horse-drawn water cart.

A sign of the times? A bullock stands beneath a Russian Oil Spirit sign in South Devon c.1940.

A former horse-drawn wagon continues in active service as late as 1955, now drawn by a tractor. The scene is hop stacking in Worcestershire.

In 1930, at the time of the NFU's warning, 80 per cent of farms were under 100 acres. This fell to around 50 per cent in 1950. By 1970 over half the farms in Britain were in excess of 100 acres with 25 per cent of these being 300 acres or more. The small acreage of British farms in the 30s and 40s relative to today, and the number of tenant farms, weighed against the introduction of modern equipment. Farm income from such small holdings simply did not justify the investment.

However, as the numbers of new tractors being produced increased in the 1930s and 40s so the numbers of second-hand machines grew. These, and the innovative use of various other vehicles, not always built for the purpose, gave small farmers the opportunity to introduce tractor power on their farms and, by the 1950s, all but a handful had been persuaded to forsake the horse for good.

Improvisation saw many hybrid vehicles on Britain's farms between the wars. Here a 1924 bull-nose Morris has been converted into a tractor in the 1930s.

"When I was a little boy I used to come outside and watch horses on the farm. There were six, then there were five, then there were none. I didn't care. I'd sooner have a tractor any day. This is just my opinion you understand. They just stick you on a tractor now and say, 'plough the field up'. Easy! You stick your old wheel down and – plough!"

Interview from *Akenfield*

Mowing in style c.1940. A pre-1914 car, complete with horn, has been fixed-up to tow a horse-drawn mower.

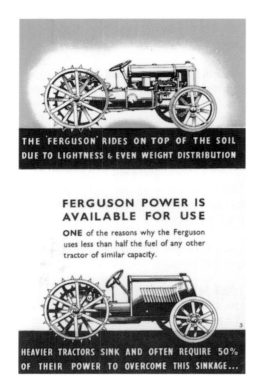

THE 'FERGUSON' RIDES ON TOP OF THE SOIL
DUE TO LIGHTNESS & EVEN WEIGHT DISTRIBUTION

**FERGUSON POWER IS
AVAILABLE FOR USE**

ONE of the reasons why the Ferguson
uses less than half the fuel of any other
tractor of similar capacity.

HEAVIER TRACTORS SINK AND OFTEN REQUIRE 50%
OF THEIR POWER TO OVERCOME THIS SINKAGE...

One of the great transformational developments in agricultural implement design appeared in the late 1920s. This was the three-point linkage, designed by Irishman Harry Ferguson. In many way this could be said to be the point at which the tractor truly superceded horse power on the farm in that the tractor could now do what the horse never could. The tool was now part of the machine that provided the power. Unlike the horse, which simply towed the cart or the plough, losing energy through complex harness and traces, the tractor now carried implements using hydraulics to lift and lower them, with fine adjustments being made possible while in motion adding to its efficiency. An initial design, the Duplex hitch had appeared in the early 1920s, with Ferguson refining this and patenting his improved design later in that decade. Easy to adjust, and to attach and remove the implements, the linkage went on to become the ubiquitous key feature on almost all modern tractors.

In 1929 Ferguson set out to build his own tractor which appeared in 1933, and for the next 20 twenty years, until selling the company in 1954, Harry Ferguson and his company remained at the forefront of tractor design and manufacturer, collaborating with many other major companies along the way, including the Ford Company of America.

The author has been fortunate in having access to the Paul Rackham collection of vintage tractors from which photographs in the book have been taken.

Ferguson Type A, manufactured in 1937 by David Brown Tractors Ltd. This version had a Coventry Climax engine and cost, at the time, £224.

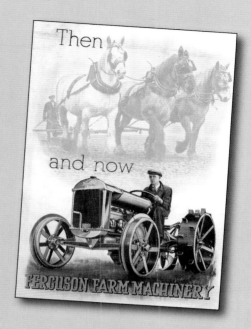

Top Left: *Close up of the Harry Ferguson's revolutionary three-point linkage. For the first time this device separated a tractor from simply being a machine that replicated the action of the horse.*

Top Centre: *A later model of the ubiquitous 'Grey Fergie', the TE-F20, manufactured in 1955. Tractors of this type, light, easy to maintain, and deliberately priced to compete against American imports, populated the fields and farmyards of Britain for much of the late twentieth century.*

Left: *Just a small percentage of the hundreds of different accessories and implements available to Ferguson tractor owners.*
All photos courtesy Paul Rackham.

Horses work alongside a tractor in 1940 as part of the Ministry of Agriculture's Plough-Up Campaign, the aim of which was to bring unproductive grassland back into cultivation. Under the scheme land that had not seen the plough since medieval times was being taken in for food production. Here, on the outskirts of suburban London a patch of ground is being made ready.

Land Army recruits are instructed in the use of a Fordson tractor c.1940.

The 1930s Depression provided for the working horse something of a reprieve, as did the following war years when fuel shortages and the need to bring more land under the plough actually saw a brief resurgence in the use of horse power. On the eve of war and with considerable prompting from farmers, the authorities recognised the importance of increasing food production at home. With lessons from the Great War still in focus – this time the U-Boat threat to imported food would be even greater – the government began to put in place their 'Plough-Up' scheme. This included a plan to bring an additional 2 million acres under the plough. To achieve this every available tractor, horse and plough would be needed.

Yet in April 1939, just four months before the outbreak of the war, it was estimated that there were only 50 000 tractors in use on British farms – and many of these dilapidated machines dating from the 1920s. This time of course there would be no commandeering of horses for the military as, by 1939, the British Army had become entirely mechanised. And the government recognised that the future lay in tractors and not horse power, and to this end they put in hand a massive programme for the supply of new machines.

In the first few months of the war 10 000 tractors and 11 000 tractor ploughs were purchased from the trade. In 1940 17 000 tractors were sold by Fordson alone, compared to 4000 in 1938. Some 2000 combine harvesters were imported, and 35 000 potato harvesters produced, mainly by British factories. By the war's end there were an additional 170 000 tractors on the country's farms. Even so, in 1942, the horse still outnumbered tractors by a factor of 30 to 1.

What now worried the authorities was the lack of available human labour. In the previous two decades thousands had deserted the land, settling in cities or emigrating, and once again young men were being called up to fight. Peter Hicks, now in his 80s and farming at Venton on Dartmoor, in 1939 lived with his three sisters on the family's farm at Kingskerswell in Devon. He recalls:

I was thirteen and a small lad for my age when the farm labourers were called up. We had six horses on the farm including, Duke, Prince, Blossom and Tidy. I was able to use them for harrowing but not for ploughing as I was too short to reach the lever that regulated the depth. To harness the shires, one was over 18 hands, I had to tie the bridle to the cart wheel and stand in the wagon to lift the straps over its back.

'*We could do with thousands more like you..*'

RECRUITING REOPENED
The Land Army has special need of Volunteers for milking and other responsible jobs

Land Girls bringing in the harvest on a Cornish farm c.1943.

The war years 1939-45 gave some respite to the decline of the horse. Fuel shortages and the bringing back into cultivation millions of acres of idle land meant that every available source of power was needed. But this was the swansong of the horse in farming, and from the 1950s onwards their disappearance was swift and relentless.

Right: *Withycombe, Somerset in 1944. A wounded Australian airmen, sent to convalesce on Higher Rodhuish Farm, helps with the harvesting.*

Below right: *Evacuees being collected from Lee Court Station, Worcestershire, by horse and cart in 1940. This is hop country and no doubt all hands were required for work during the hop picking season.*

Below: *US soldiers visit the blacksmith in Burton Bradstock, Dorset, 1944.*

Above: *Every available machine was put to work during the war. Here, ancient tractors provided by the War Agricultural Executive Committee ('WarAgs') clear gorse from land to be brought into cultivation at St Ervan in Cornwall c.1940. Right: A horse-drawn binder that's seen better days is brought into service during the war. Below: Horse and tractor power work alongside locals and prisoners-of-war at Chipley in Somerset c.1943.*

Laura Knight's wartime painting made for a Women's Land Army poster.

Conscription left farming short of some 50 000 workers and among those drafted in to fill their place were members of the Women's Land Army. By the first month of war 17 000 women had been recruited, their numbers rising through conscription to over 80 000 in 1945. One such was seventeen year old Maud Shire whose memoir *A Country War* records life on a Devon farm in 1943:

> *We didn't have anything mechanised; no car, no tractor, no engines of any kind. All field work was carried out manually or by huge working shire horses. I was introduced to 'Bob', a medium sized very dark brown mare. Bob turned out to have a very unpredictable nature and at times refused point blank to work, or even to move when the mood took her.*

The war was kind to many farmers who benefited from the work they had done in bringing so much land back into production and from the supply of food to a hungry nation. Those who did profit were able to take advantage of the post-war boom in which, as the size of farms increased, so did the move towards complete mechanisation. Even though a quarter of a million horses were still in use in agriculture in the early 1950s, for the first time in history they were outnumbered by tractors. For the new breed of progressive farmer the horse was a relic of the past, and by the 1970s the sight of a working horse in British farming had become a cause for public curiosity and comment. The age of the horse was over.

We approach the end of this chapter with photographs from the 1950s and 60s accompanying memories by friend and fellow author, Roger Fogg, recollecting his boyhood in those years, the dying days of working horses in Cornwall:

There were still some farmers who kept their horses long after tractors and other mechanical contrivances had taken over the traditional tasks allotted to the beasts. For some it was a matter of simple economics, perhaps a refusal to see that the old ways had gone for good, or even the fact that a good and faithful servant could not be summarily got rid of. Well into the nineteen fifties horses could still be observed in fields, often brought out of retirement for more delicate tasks like carefully walking between rows of potatoes so that they could be weeded, or using a harvester to spin the potatoes out of the ground. They were sometimes seen working alongside tractors, often with older men using them on buck rakes to gather in loose hay for the stationary baler, or perhaps on the hay grab where the only task required of them was to walk backwards and forwards at harvest time lifting loose hay up the pole and on to a rick. The big cart horses were sometimes also harnessed up to wagons and paraded at village carnivals, towing the carnival queen and her attendants on their beautifully decorated floats, or leading the silver band with their gleaming harness and well groomed flanks.

It is October 1964 at the tail end of the horse's life in farming. The distant tractor moves along the rows towards the pickers while horses and carts arrive to pick up the potatoes.

Bringing in the hay, 1952.

Ask most people of a certain age about their memories of working horses and they will invariably say they can recall the time when a man and his horse and cart would regularly do the rounds delivering groceries, coal, and even soft drinks, and perhaps the rag and bone man, calling out as his cart clattered around the streets. Some, as children, remember staring up at the giant horse which seemed to know where to stop and where to walk on as it came to each house. A few of these traders continued beyond the 1950s and 60s, but now are a thing of the past.

Here the local fruit and veg seller, Mr Corke, serves his customer in Appledore, Devon, in 1953. His horse, 12-year-old 'Dolly' was a firm favourite with the local children.

Just occasionally however you could get a glimpse of the old ways of working, the traditional concept of looking at a horse more as a means to an end than a creature of power and beauty.

A pair of big Suffolk Punches was owned locally by a farmer who cared much more for them than for his old Standard Fordson tractor. Having purchased the machine through the government lease-lend system during the war, he had to admit that it had its plus side, but it was absolutely no substitute for his beloved horses. He could not get the tractor to stop when he shouted 'Whoa!' and had a partially demolished wall as a result. The Suffolks were kept in a dark stable; the windows covered in ivy, swallows and sparrows nesting in the spidery rafters, cobbles on the floor and stalls either side of the centre aisle. The hay racks, rusting semi circular attachments nailed precariously to the walls, were always heaped full of good hay whilst a drink of fresh water was

provided for each individual. Both racks and drinkers would be daily cleared of the rubbish that seemed to fall into them on a regular basis. Miscellaneous bits of harness were hung on nails, long ropes used as reins were coiled up ready for use, whilst outside there was always a spare cartwheel and a set of used hoop-like tyres. The ropes incidentally could be borrowed to use for lashing to branches and swinging in great arcs from the tops of hedges, as long as they didn't break and were returned to their place in the stable after use. The stable was lit by a single light bulb, smelled singularly of horses, a quite distinct odour that was so different from cows, chickens, sheep or pigs, and the whole building was warmed by the body heat of its incumbents.

The horses were used regularly in preference to the tractor. There were a lot of ancient bits of machinery that still had long draw bars. Most farmers cut these off and substituted some form of tow hitch, but you could still see the attachments on hay cutters, seed drills and the like around the farmyard or parked up in the mowhay (a kind of meadow next the farm buildings where machinery was kept, fowls housed and hay ricks or silage pits constructed). The animals, although loved and cared for were not pristine in any way. Grooming was minimal and after a hard day's work in the fields, the animals would be put away, still with the accumulated muck and mud on them. Patting them would produce great clouds of dust, whilst stroking them just got you a handful of coarse hair. Their feet were enormous and dangerous. The iron-shod hooves

Leading a horse over steep ground while hoeing at Silverton, Devon, 1962.

Three-horse team pulling a reaper, Trevescan near Sennen, Cornwall 1950s.

Two young girls hitching a ride on 'Prince'
c. 1950.

could make a mess of your own feet if they were crushed, and the farmers toes were permanently black and blue as a result. The eyes were, unblinkered at least, watery but bright, and their teeth were frightful, yellow and brown things that clanged together like a gin trap within a set of wet frothy lips.

My best mate and I sometimes used to hitch a ride on the back of the horses, one each, as they pulled the loaded carts along. It's not that easy to get up on to a full grown Suffolk Punch; heaving yourself up using various bits of leather strap and dangling chains on to the shafts, then trying to find a comfortable spot either on the blanket, or the actual harness whilst holding on to the two bits of upright iron that guided the reins. Once there, it felt extremely high off the ground, and you really didn't want to fall off. The harness at the time had seen better days and the stitching had come undone to reveal the straw used inside as packing. The backs of the Suffolks were very wide and moved unpredictably, so you had to hold on tight. There was an awful lot of snot and dribble coming your way, and what with the farts and seemingly endless amount of small ginger coloured horse flies that stung any bits of equine or human flesh they could find meant that the experience was not as romantic as some might wish it to be remembered.

Bill Thorn ploughing at Rattery with 'Prince'
and 'Ruby' in South Devon in 1954, watched
by Jean and John Thorn.

Inevitably time took its toll, the farmer eventually had to retire and give up his land. The horses succumbed to old age, at least that was what was said, and mechanisation finally ruled the roost. The stable and yard still exist, but at the time of writing is up for sale, with planning permission to convert to luxury holiday flats. Across the lane the brand new milking parlour and vast hanger-like barns owe little to the days of the horse and cart.

*   *   *

Suffolk Horses at Somerleyton Hall in Suffolk where they are used on the estate farm.
Photo courtesy Edward Knowles.

There are of course those who today are keeping alive the spirit of the working horse, determined to preserve this important aspect of our heritage, more often than not born out of a passion for horses and a fascination for the traditions involved in the various aspects of farm work. Ploughing competitions provide opportunities for entrants to test and hone their skills, the high point of the British season being the British National Ploughing Championships organised by the Society of Ploughmen.

At agricultural shows throughout Britain it is unusual for there not to be a specialist section for working horses, with preserved vintage vehicles often being a feature of

Somerleyton Suffolks at plough.
Photo courtesy Edward Knowles.

Watercolour sketch by Elizabeth Kitson SEA.

the main event. Each of our native types of heavy horse now has its own society or trust whose members are dedicated to the preservation of the breed. The Suffolk Punch, for instance, was once so close to extinction that it appeared on the list of endangered species. The Suffolk Punch Trust, set up in 2002, has since done much to secure the breed's survival and similar work is being done by other groups to ensure future generation can enjoy watching these magnificent animals at work. Good work is also being done by various commercial organisations, often those with visitor attractions which include heavy horses at work, while various museums offer further insight into the history of the working horse.

There are many individuals who, out of preference, still work with horses, one such group being the British Horse Loggers. These full- and part-time professional forestry workers use horses by choice in order to preserve low environmental impact within the industry.

Both in this book and *The War Horses* I touched briefly on the importance of the horse in art and the cultural significance of this historically. Many contemporary artists also keep this traditional alive, none more so that the Society of Equestrian Artists whose members produce some of the most powerful work in contemporary British art, both in painting and sculpture.

These and many other individuals and organisation would require a book of their own in order to do them justice but publications such as the excellent *Heavy Horse World Magazine* do keep the public regularly informed of news and events in what continues to be a vibrant arena.

A Lost World

European unemployment rates are now at a record high.
One in five people under the age of twenty-five have no job.

Source: Finfacts July 2012

The working horse has had its day. Centuries of how things had always been were, in less than half a century, swept away. And now the last generation to witness its passing is itself nearing an end. Surely we have little reason to mourn for, as we have seen, the age of the horse tied many of those employed in farming to a life of poverty, hunger and crippling labour. Yet we find in the image of the horse and horseman tracing long furrows across a meadow, or families working together in the fields, inherently picturesque. Nostalgic.

Look back at the photographs in this book; at the harvest workers poised to catch the camera's eye, the horses patiently nearby. Here we catch a glimpse of the reason

The future approaches. A car speeds down the street past a horse and cart sitting outside the Castle Inn, West Coker c.1920.

GOODBYE OLD FRIEND

for our wistfulness. These faces from the past have dignity, a pride in each knowing they play their part in carrying out the everyday task. In doing things well, together.

And the horsemen, whispering arcane words into their charges' ears. Horses that stood, walked, stopped, or pulled with all their might at each command – man and beast together. Little wonder that we should feel some sadness that we never saw them thus. That we can never be part of their lost world.

The machines that drove the horse away, provide us with more food than we can eat, add years to our lives and make our children tall and strong. Little brothers of these machines now sit neatly in our hands, bring us pictures and send messages from around the world. They whisper in our ears.

The men leaned on their rakes, about to begin.
But still. And all were silent. All was old.
This morning time, with a great age untold,
Older than Clare and Cowper, Morland and Crome,
Than, at the field's edge, the farmer's home.
A white house crouched at the foot of a great tree,
Under the heavens that know not what years be
The men, the beasts, the trees, the implements...

From 'Haymaking' Edward Thomas